FE!

I

THE STORY OF
Robert Louis Stevenson

*Leerie propped his ladder against the lamppost
and waved back*

THE STORY OF
Robert Louis Stevenson

By JOAN HOWARD

Illustrated by JO POLSENO

ENID LAMONTE MEADOWCROFT
Supervising Editor

PUBLISHERS Grosset & Dunlap NEW YORK

PRINTED IN THE UNITED STATES OF AMERICA
Library of Congress Catalog Card No. 58-5704

Contents

[v]

CONTENTS

Illustrations

THE STORY OF

Robert Louis Stevenson

Barefooted, Smout tiptoed down the stairs

CHAPTER ONE

The Land of Counterpane

IN EDINBURGH, Scotland, No. 17 Heriot Row stood as dignified and four-square as its gray stone neighbors. But one upstairs room was quite different. That room contained The Land of Counterpane, a country exactly the size of a small boy's bed.

Today, The Land of Counterpane was in a state of mutiny. Its little monarch jerked his knees, and toy houses and pasteboard trees slithered down patchwork quilt hillsides. Lead soldiers tumbled into a heap, friend and enemy together. A tin trumpet hit the floor with a clatter.

Robert Louis Stevenson was not having a temper tantrum. But he was very tired of staying in bed. He looked anxiously at his father with enormous dark eyes.

[3]

"Truly, Papa, I am not sick. Can't you see I'm simply bursting with health? Let me get up, and I'll show you. I could run all the way up the hill to the Castle. I could swim down the Water of Leith right out to sea. I could fight highwaymen or pirates or—"

A cough broke off his words. When he could speak, he explained it away. "Just a frog in my throat. A very *little* frog."

Gently, Mr. Thomas Stevenson pushed his six-year-old son back against the pillows. "Now, Smout, you are not to excite yourself," he said. "That is no way to get better."

"Smout" was Mr. Stevenson's pet name for Robert Louis. It was the Scots word for young salmon, and it fitted the lively child. He was as quick and alert as a fish. And as thin as a young salmon, too, because of having so many feverish colds.

"If I *must* stay in bed, then—and it's unfair when I'm perfectly well—you must tell me another story," he demanded. "Then Cummie will tell me a story. And Mama can come and tell me a story, and then—"

"Bless the bairn!" his nurse, Alison Cunningham, broke in. "There are not so many stories in the world as he wants to hear."

"Oh, surely, Cummie, there must be?"

Smout was alarmed at the very idea of a day when there would be no new stories.

Mr. Stevenson chuckled. "Never fear, Smout, there are more stories in the world than anybody can listen to. There are even a number of my own you have yet to hear."

Smout's brown eyes shone. His father's stories were about the sea—ships and smugglers and wrecks along Scotland's rocky coast. Mr. Stevenson followed the family tradition in being a designer and builder of lighthouses. So his stories of wild crags and roaring surf were not only exciting but true.

That day, however, there was to be no story told to Smout, though a quite remarkable story would be told. It began when his mother came into the room.

"There's a letter from your Uncle David," she said, "with news for you, Smout. He is offering a prize to all his nephews and nieces for the best *History of Moses*."

Smout sat bolt upright in bed. "That's easy —I know *all* about Moses! Cummie read me his story from the Bible. I'm sure to win the prize, Mama. I shall draw pictures to go with my stories. None of the others will think of that."

The others were Smout's cousins, and he

had fifty of them. He was one of the youngest, but that didn't bother him. He was too busy deciding how to make his history of Moses the most exciting story in the world to worry about what his older cousins could do.

It didn't matter, either, that Smout hadn't yet learned to write. His mother must write it all down for him, and his father could see that she didn't leave out any bits. And Cummie must bring his drawing paper and paintbox—

"I'll draw them marching out of Egypt with their camels. You must not be frightened, Mama, but I'm going to make the seven plagues simply horrendous! Are you ready, Mama? Do you have quantities of paper?"

Robert Louis Stevenson started his first story. He remembered everything Cummie had read to him about Moses. But it was still very much his own story, with his own ideas of how it ought to be told—a little bit funny and very, very exciting.

In his pictures the Israelites fleeing from the Egyptians wore top hats, like Papa's Sunday best. Moses smoked a pipe while he led his people with enormous dignity. Smout's camels had very skinny legs and very long noses, but there was no mistaking the big humps on their backs.

"I'm sure Uncle David will recognize them, even if he has seen real camels and I haven't," he said when he had finished. "You do like the story, don't you?"

His mother liked it, and his father said he was proud of Smout. Cummie said it was a wonderful story, but now hadn't he better rest until she brought his supper?

"Oh, no!" Smout was shocked. "I'm not the tiniest bit tired. I never get tired when I'm having fun. Anyway, it's time for Leerie."

Watching for the lamplighter every evening was Smout's special treat. He knelt upon the window seat, listening. At last there was a stomping and clatter. Leerie was coming through the dusk with lantern and ladder.

Smout felt lucky living at No. 17 because it had a street lamp in front of the house. With his forehead against the windowpane, he waved to Leerie. When Leerie propped his ladder against the lamppost, he looked up and waved back. Then he climbed to touch the lamp into a bright crocus blossom of light.

"Magic!" Every night Smout was entranced by this. "Isn't it wonderful, Papa, to make a light in the dark so people will be safe?"

Mr. Stevenson, whose lighthouses sent beams over black seas to make the night safe for mariners, agreed that it was wonderful.

When Leerie had gone, Papa and Mama said good night. Cummie brought Smout's supper and allowed no dawdling over the rice pudding.

"I'll never, never be able to go to sleep, Cummie," Smout pleaded when she was tucking in his blankets. "Won't you . . . ?"

"No stories tonight. You are already over-tired. Lie quiet, and you'll drop off to sleep, never fear." Cummie lit the night candle in its red glass bowl and blew out the lamp.

How could a boy sleep when thoughts kept chasing each other around in his head? One thought was particularly teasing, because Smout could not quite catch it. It was something to do with his *History of Moses*, but what?

Smout decided he could never capture that provoking thought in bed. Perhaps if he were outside where he could look at the stars, he would find the answer there. And even if that did not work, it would be an adventure to be out in the dark night.

As he slipped out of bed, the flickering night light stretched his shadow like a giant. Barefooted, Smout tiptoed down the stairs. His parents were talking in the parlor. They

Cummie had already missed him

did not hear him even when the front door creaked as he pulled it open. Then he was out side.

Smout danced down the garden path, gazing up at millions of stars twinkling in a black velvet sky. Suddenly the thought that had been playing hide-and-seek with him was there, as sharp and clear as the stars above. Just in time too, for Cummie had already missed him. An open door spilled yellow lamplight onto the path. Voices were calling.

It did not take long to capture the small boy and pack him back to bed. From Edinburgh Castle high on the hill, the golden notes of the evening bugle proclaimed nine o'clock. The music joined the glory of the stars, shining and bright, still going round and round in his head. Smout was content.

No longer need he be afraid that Cummie or his father would run out of stories. That teasing thought about the *History of Moses* had given him the answer.

"When they have no more stories, I'll make up my own," he told himself comfortably

The young Teller of Tales fell asleep. He dreamed of listening to a pen scratching on paper. The pen was his mother's. But the words it wrote were his own.

CHAPTER TWO

Adventure at Colinton Manse

ROBERT LOUIS was a delicate child, with all his coughs and fevers. His grandfather, the Reverend Lewis Balfour, knew it. So did Aunt Jane, who kept house for her father at Colinton Manse and welcomed scores of nephews and nieces there. Probably all the older ones among his forty Balfour and ten Stevenson cousins knew it. Robert Louis flatly denied it.

On a late summer day, a dozen of his cousins would have laughed at the idea of him being sickly. As usual at Colinton, Robert Louis was a ringleader in every game, for all he was not quite seven years old.

"Cut down the scurvy beggars! Charge, men, CHARGE!" That shrill command did not sound delicate.

[*11*]

"Mind the water, Lou!" Delhi Lewis shouted a warning.

Five Balfour cousins had been named Lewis for their grandfather. To tell them apart they had nicknames, taken from the places where they were born. Delhi Lewis and Poona Lewis and Cramond Lewis were at Colinton.

Robert Louis had been named for both his grandfathers—Robert Lewis Balfour Stevenson. Then the spelling of his second name was changed to *Louis*. His cousins all called him Lou.

Delhi Lewis' warning came too late. Lou was wading through the river called the Water of Leith to attack the enemy on the flank. Mindful of their grandfather's orders to keep out of the river, his gallant band did not follow. It did not matter. As General and Army combined, Lou felt a match for any foe.

"Surrender, or I'll blast ye to perdition!" he shouted.

"But, Lou," his cousin Henrietta called. "We're not soldiers! We're being smugglers today!"

"I've changed all that," replied General Stevenson, clambering up on the bank. "But," he added with his next breath, "if it's smugglers you want to be, follow me! We'll dig up those

casks of French wine we buried on yonder
isle . . ."

Once again he plunged into the water, this
time where it ran slow and dark below the
mill. He was on his way to a tiny, sluicy island.

Forgetting Grandfather, the others followed
his ringing command. Wet to the waist, they
scrambled onto the little island. As daredevil
smugglers they stomped up and down till the
treacherous yellow sand moved under their
feet. Gradually the ground flattened out level
with the river. Dark brown water washed up
around their legs.

"Quicksand!" shouted Louis. "Jump for
your lives!"

A dangerous stampede brought them
splashing through the water to the riverbank.
But not completely out of danger, for their
grandfather was waiting there.

The Reverend Lewis Balfour was a fine
grandfather, but a stern one. The scolding
they got was one to remember. And it was
worst for Louis. The smuggler chief was
handed over to Aunt Jane to be put to bed so
he would not take cold.

"Truly, Aunt Jane," he protested, "I had
no idea it would be quicksand. It was such a
lovely place to be marooned."

"The chief of our Aunts," as Lou called her smiled at her naughty nephew. "You think marooning your cousins is safe, do you? Yesterday it was slaying dragons you thought wa safe. And look what that led to."

"Och, I wasn't slaying dragons," Louis said "I *was* the dragon. And that silly old horse should never have bolted. I didn't ever breathe fire at him—really. I only snorted and used my red handkerchief to wave about like flames."

"Poona Lewis has a fine lump on his head to show for it," Aunt Jane said, pulling off Louis' sopping stockings.

"I know that," Louis admitted. "But St. George shouldn't let his horse throw him."

"There was Tuesday, too," Aunt Jane reminded him, "when you and Willie both got sick eating buttercups, which are quite poisonous."

"We were shipwrecked and had no other food," Louis explained.

Aunt Jane had to laugh as she bundled the little boy into bed. "What about that evening last week when you and Willie and Henrietta bolted into the house frightened half out of your wits? Was that a game too?"

One thing that made Colinton Manse so exciting was the churchyard. It lay just beyond and above the garden, on a level with the top of the eight-foot wall. They could see the tombstones and were always on the lookout for ghosts which they called "spunkies." Louis invented scary games to play under the wall. He called the path there the Witches' Walk.

The evening Aunt Jane was asking about, he and Willie and Henrietta had been out on the Witches' Walk at dusk. Suddenly, they saw a burning eye looking out from a hole high in the wall. Louis discovered it, and then the others saw it, too.

"Is it a spunkie?" Henrietta whispered, peering up at it.

"More likely a bird of ill omen perching in a cranny," Willie said.

"I think," Louis said softly, "that hole goes through into a grave. And yon's a dead man sitting up in his coffin watching us."

At last they brought the gardener's wheelbarrow around the big black yew tree and placed it close to the wall. One after another, they climbed up to look into the hole. Not a word was said. When Henrietta got down last, all three children took to their heels. They had arrived panting in the dining room.

They never did know what they had seen.

*They saw a burning eye looking out from
a hole in the wall*

They had not even talked about it again, so Louis certainly could not explain to Aunt Jane. But one of Aunt Jane's charms was that she knew some questions could not be answered.

Now she tucked the covers up under his chin.

"You ought to try to stay out of trouble, Lou," she said. "If your mother knew what mischief you get into here, I doubt if she'd let you visit us. And you do like to come to Colinton, don't you?"

"Oh, I do!" Nowhere but at Colinton did Louis know a lawn like a saucerful of sunshine all summer long. Nowhere but in Colinton Wood was there such a merry chorus of blackbirds and thrushes. There were pools and river for paddling, and stable and coachhouse to play in. Yes, Colinton was wonderful. Louis was glad he didn't have to go back to Edinburgh for another fortnight.

"This is the best visit ever," he told Aunt Jane.

That was so, for Louis' cousins had greeted him with new respect. He had won Uncle David's prize for his *History of Moses*—a book of Bible stories with lots of pictures. Louis had told his cousins, and now he told Aunt Jane,

[*17*]

that when he wasn't too busy being a pirate he
was going to write stories for everybody to
read.

"It wouldn't surprise me if you do turn out
to be an author," Aunt Jane said. "But if this
is leading up to you wanting me to copy down
one of your stories now, I'll have to disappoint
you. The maids have been giving the parlor a
thorough cleaning, and the furniture is out on
the lawn. I must go and dust it before they
carry it back indoors."

"Oh, do let me see!" Louis was surprised,
for he had been brought in from the river by

the back door. In a flash he was out of bed and at the window. "How silly it looks! They've set all the tables and chairs just as if they were still in a room, only without walls. Aunt Jane, can't we pretend there are walls? Then I can rest on the sofa while you dust."

Before Aunt Jane had time to say "yes" or "no," he was on his way outside.

Naturally, he did not stay quietly on the sofa very long.

"What on earth is that?" he asked when Aunt Jane opened the glass door of a cabinet and carefully used her feather duster on a white, skeleton-looking bone.

"It is the wing bone of an albatross," she replied. "So you should have said, 'What in the sky is that?'"

"Is an albatross a bird? Surely it can't be— this is much too big."

"Yes, it is a bird. This one had a wing span of seventeen feet—wider than many a little house," Aunt Jane told Louis.

Then Aunt Jane had to tell him a great deal more about the white birds that often slept on the wing over vast southern seas. Sailors considered them lucky and were glad to have an albatross follow their ships. Waving her duster, Aunt Jane recited a long poem

bout an Ancient Mariner who shot an alba-
ross with his crossbow and had bad luck for-
ver after.

Louis wanted to know more and more about
he giant birds and the lonely seas. Aunt Jane
old him of coral islands dotting the enormous
Pacific Ocean. And about jungle islands where
man-eating savages lived.

"That's wonderful," Louis murmured.
Then and there he made himself a promise.
Some day he would sail across that ocean and
have an albatross follow him like a pet. He
would visit every island, even where the cannibals lived.

"I'm sure I could make friends with cannibals," he told Aunt Jane as they went indoors together. "You see, I'd be very careful
not to land until after their dinnertime."

CHAPTER THREE

Happy Birthday

BACK in Edinburgh, Louis was lonely. After Colinton Manse, the house in Heriot Row seemed too big and too dark for just one small boy and a few grownups.

Often, when the wind shrieked around corners, Louis had nightmares—particularly if he had been naughty. The worst was a horseman who came riding furiously up from the bottom of the street after him. The horseman was dressed all in black with a cloak pulled over his face. His steed was as black as midnight.

One night, Louis tossed and squirmed in his bed, trying to escape. But in this dream, he could not run. The horseman was breaking into the house, with clanking bit and stirrups, when Louis woke with a yelp of fright.

"Now, now, Master Lou." In a moment, Cummie's warm hand held his chilled little paw. "You've been dreaming and fair waked the house with your moans."

"Oh, Cummie, the horseman almost got me just before you came!"

"Hush, now," Cummie's voice was gentle. "We'll never let him catch you."

She turned up the lamp and sat down beside his bed. Louis saw that she had the big Bible with her. A story from the Bible always chased away his hobgoblins. How clever Cummie was to know! How kind she was not to re-

[23]

mind him that nightmares might not come i
he weren't naughty!

The wind still howled, and rain beat a tat
too on the window. But it was only an ordi
nary storm now. Cummie went on reading
Before Louis went back to sleep, he heard rea
horses. Country carts were beginning to rum
ble over the cobblestones bringing butter and
eggs to the city markets. Horses neighed, and
drivers called to one another. To Louis, the
racket was the promise of a new day. It lulled
him to sleep.

Storm clouds and winds were gone when he
wakened. The sun threw pale lozenges of light
across his carpet. Cummie brought breakfast,
and meant to stay and see that he ate it to the
last crumb.

"Then you'll have to tell me a story to make
this porridge slip down my throat," Louis said.
"Otherwise I shall probably choke on a
lump."

Cummie's eyes twinkled. To tease him, she
pretended that she thought it was another
Bible story he wanted. Louis stared at her in
astonishment.

"Why, Cummie, it's daylight now! Let's
have pirates!"

"Pirates on the tenth of November?" Cummie asked.

Louis was puzzled.

"Pirates and you," Cummie explained, "somehow always lead to mischief. It would not be wise to get into mischief on the tenth of November, or the eleventh, or the twelfth—"

Louis whooped. "Oh, only three more days! I *will* have to be good."

Only three more days to November thirteenth, and that was his birthday.

For the next three days, Mr. and Mrs. Stevenson smiled to see how good their son had grown. He even rested when he was told, at least most of the time. By the evening of the twelfth, Louis was practically bursting with all the energy he had stored up. Strange muffled noises from downstairs added to his excitement. Nobody would answer questions, and for the life of him he could not guess what was going on.

At daybreak the noise was explained. Louis wakened from a dream that Cummie was washing his face with a wet sponge. He found that his face *was* being washed, but the sponge was the pink tongue of an excitable Skye terrier puppy.

"Coolin!" Louis cried with delight. "Oh, Coolin!"

The name just came to him. The wriggly puppy accepted it as a fine name he would recognize anywhere as his own. The bed became such a tangle of happy boy and happy dog that Cummie had quite a time straightening them out for breakfast.

Coolin was Louis' first dog, so it was an hour before he so much as looked at other birthday gifts. When he did open them, there were two particularly wonderful presents. One was an enormous box of lead soldiers, wearing the gay kilts of all the famous Scottish regiments. The other was a sword from Aunt Jane. What a sword it was! Not just a wooden toy, but real metal with a silver hilt and silver on the scabbard.

"You look like a general," his mother said when he buckled it on. "I do hope it is not too heavy for you."

Louis instantly proved it was not too heavy. His father backed him up. "Fine sword, Smout! Now look at these stone blocks. You could build a lighthouse with them."

"Or a fortress!" Louis said. Some day, very likely, he would build real lighthouses like his grandfather and his uncles and his father. His

What a sword it was!

family were always called the Lighthouse Ste
vensons. But today, how could he think of any
thing except a battle? He had an army o
soldiers at his command, a real sword hangin;
at his side, and Coolin for mascot.

A battle it was! All that raw, foggy day
Louis marched and attacked. He shouted or
ders until he was hoarse. Indoors and out th
fight raged, the heavy sword clanging, Coolir
barking encouragement to his general and de
fiance to the enemy. His elders tried to put ar
end to the game. When they could not, the
bundled him into a big shawl.

"Do you think it looks like a night march?"
he asked anxiously. "It's more like a cloak thar
a shawl, isn't it?"

Louis was happy and excited. He was far too
busy to notice that his father was using the
blocks to build a little model of his owr
Skerryvore Lighthouse. He still hoped to catch
Louis' attention with it.

CHAPTER FOUR
The Kingdom of Skelt

QUITE SUDDENLY, Louis found No. 17 Heriot Row an entirely new place. His cousin Bob came to spend the winter with him. The house that was too big and too dark for one boy was just right for two boys and a puppy.

Robert Alan Mowbray Stevenson was Louis' favorite cousin. He was a bit older, but he had precisely the same ideas of fun. Every game now was twice as exciting and more than twice as noisy. Even the nightmare horseman didn't dare break in when Bob shared Louis' bedroom.

It did not matter that for weeks on end Louis could not go outdoors. The raw, smoky air that made people call Edinburgh "Auld Reekie" was chillier and foggier than usual.

But Bob never minded staying inside with Louis. They built forts and played at soldiers. They upended chairs to make ships. Once they decided the staircase would make a splendid stormy sea. It did.

Never before had the dignified house heard such an uproar, such clatter and bumping. Mrs. Stevenson and Cummie, Cook and the housemaids all came running. They found Bob and Louis picking themselves up out of their splintered chair-ship at the foot of the stairs. Coolin was yelping because he was on the bottom of the heap.

"You've been saved, Coolin," Louis comforted him. "When you're a ship's mascot, you've got to expect shipwreck now and again."

"Mark my words, those bairns will kill themselves yet," Cook predicted.

When they found out the boys weren't hurt beyond a few bruises, Cummie and Mrs. Stevenson were very cross. They said the boys would have to stay in their own room all day tomorrow. And no sweets for dessert for three days.

"It's a good thing we were wrecked on a lee shore, shipmate," Louis told his cousin. "Otherwise it might have been serious."

The next day they spent painting pictures of tropical isles. They put in pirates burying treasure and cannibals peering out of bushes.

"You know, Bob, I think islands are the best places in the world," Louis said. "When I have my own kingdom, it's going to be an island."

"Mine is, too," Bob agreed. So they invented two rival kingdoms and called them *Nosingtonia* and *Encyclopedia.*

One morning at breakfast, Cummie eyed a bowl in which the oatmeal was buried beneath a mountain of sugar. "Master Bob, I'll thank you to stop playing about in your porridge," she said.

"You forget, Cummie," Louis said. "We aren't Bob and Lou any more. Bob is King of Nosingtonia and I am the King of Encyclopedia. The King of Nosingtonia's porridge is a country covered by snow. There is no springtime there, and the snow never melts."

"Indeed," said Cummie, "and what might *Your* Majesty be doing, splashing that milk about in your bowl?"

"Oh, in my country floods are eating away the land. Like this." Louis' spoon jabbed at his oatmeal so milk crept in through caves and tunnels. It made a fine sloshy mess altogether.

"I'll still thank both Your Majesties to finish your breakfast and let me clear away," Cummie declared. "It's a fine morning, too, for a change. I might let the two of you go to play in Queens Street Gardens."

They finished breakfast in short order.

But playing in the park was too babyish for the young monarchs. They decided to walk all the way to the harbor where the Water of Leith ran into the arm of the sea called the Firth of Forth.

"We can inspect our navies there," Louis said. On the way, the two kings began discussing treaties to be signed. Louis, Encyclopedia Rex, said he was willing to trade his Pine Islands for one thousand yards of Grundrungia cloth and an air gun.

Then he stopped in his tracks. Gone were all thoughts of trading and ships and kingdoms. He stood staring into the small show-window of Mr. Smith's stationery store at the corner of Leith Walk.

ROBERT LOUIS STEVENSON

A model theater was set up there, all re
and gilt pasteboard. Around it hung sheet
with scenes on them to cut out: "A Forest Set."
"A Combat." "Soldiers Carousing." And
many, many more. A boy might buy these
plays if he had pocket money, for the sig
read: *Penny Plain and Twopence Colored*

As it happened, Bob and Lou each had a
penny Cummie had given them to buy buns
at the pastry cook's. They pressed their noses
against the glass to see better. "We wouldn't
have to buy colored ones," Louis mused. "So

we could each have one and paint our own. They'd be as good as Mr. Skelt's."

"Who's Mr. Skelt?" Bob wanted to know.

"The man who makes them." Louis pointed to the publisher's name in small print. "What do you think, Bob—shall we?"

For answer, Bob opened the shop door, setting three little bells to jangling above it. Inside, the place seemed dark.

"It smells like wet Bibles," Louis whispered.

Mr. Smith eyed them suspiciously. "What can I do for you young gentlemen? The plays? You are intending to buy, not merely look at them, I hope."

Bob and Louis showed him their pennies. Then he allowed them to make a choice among his whole stock of plays. It wasn't easy when there were so many. "Aladdin." "The Red Rover." "The Smuggler." "Robin Hood." "The Inchcape Bell." "Three-fingered Jack, The Terror of Jamaica." And many more besides.

"I don't know whether to take 'Three-fingered Jack' or 'The Smuggler,' " Louis said finally. "Which one are you buying, Bob?"

" 'Robin Hood.' It has lots of forest scenes."

"An excellent choice." Mr. Smith quickly

[35]

took the play from Bob's fingers. "I shall wrap it for you. And you, young sir, I'd recommend 'Three-fingered Jack.' Very popular, that one is."

When he had both their pennies, Mr. Smith grew friendlier. To produce the plays properly, he pointed out, it was necessary to have the model theater which he also sold. The price he named left them gasping. Never would they be able to save enough pocket money to buy it.

It was Coolin who unexpectedly came to the rescue.

At that very moment there was a furious barking and scratching at the shop door. In came Mr. Stevenson with Louis' terrier tugging at his leash.

"There was no keeping him in the house after you left," Mr. Stevenson said. "I finally had to bring him out to track you. He's good at that."

Mr. Smith was suddenly genial. He took down a box and set up a model theater on the counter.

"The young gentlemen have purchased two of Mr. Skelt's plays," he told Louis' father. "We were discussing the price of the heater in which to present them. Perhaps, ir, you would care to . . ."

Mr. Stevenson bought the theater. "I think ve shall have the twopence colored 'Inchcape Bell,' " he added. "That is the legend of the eef where your grandfather built Bell Rock Lighthouse, boys."

"Then we must have it, Papa," Louis declared. "And we shan't have to stop to paint scenery, so we can give that play right away."

Louis presented his first play that same evening. When tea was cleared away, the cook and two housemaids and the boot boy all came upstairs to join Mr. and Mrs. Stevenson and Cummie as audience.

Bob arranged the lamps to throw light on the stage. Coolin wanted to help, but Mr. Stevenson collared him and held him on his lap. Then Bob, behind the scenes, worked the pasteboard figures while Louis recited the ballad that went with the action on the stage.

With much feeling, he told of shipwrecks on the Inchcape Rock. A good abbot put a bell on a float there to warn mariners away. But wicked Sir Ralph the Rover, who looted wrecks, cut the bell from Inchcape Rock and it sank into the sea. Years afterward, in a fear-

ful storm, Sir Ralph himself was wrecked on
that reef. Louis had remembered every word
of the long ballad, and he brought it to a fine
dramatic close:

> *"But even in his dying fear,*
> *One dreadful sound could the Rover hear,*
> *A sound as if with the Inchcape Bell*
> *The devil below was ringing his knell."*

"And serve him right," said Cummie. She
and the rest of the audience clapped and
clapped. Donal, the boot boy, cheered until
Cook had to shush him.

Louis beamed at them all. That day he had
found a brand-new kingdom. He called it the
Kingdom of Skelt.

CHAPTER FIVE

Lighthouse Stevensons

THE Kingdom of Skelt proved even more
exciting than the Kingdoms of Nosingtonia
and Encyclopedia. Mr. Smith grew very
friendly with Bob and Louis. They were
spending all their pocket money at his store.

On rainy days they lay on the nursery
floor in front of a crackling fire to paint new
scenes and costumes for the "penny plain"
plays.

"Hi, Bob, look what an elegant purple I've
made for King Richard's royal robes," Louis
said, mixing crimson and blue in a saucer.

Coolin came to look, too. Then he sat
down in the saucer. The royal purple looked
less elegant on the fur of his hindquarters.

"He's exactly like a clown wearing purple

pantaloons," Bob declared. He and Louis laughed until they rolled on the floor, hooting and hiccuping.

Coolin objected to being laughed at. With sulky dignity, he stalked an imaginary fly. Stalking a fly in purple pantaloons was funnier than ever. The boys soon had stitches in their sides that hurt.

"Now we have to make up with Coolin," Louis said when he could talk again. He went downstairs and begged a kipper from Cook.

Coolin was offended, but kippered herrings were his favorite food. His nose twitched. He brought his nose closer to make sure it smelled what he thought it did. The kipper vanished in two big gulps.

Coolin gave Louis a few fishy licks to prove he held no hard feelings. He wagged a purple tail. That set the boys off again. "Did you ever see a purple wag before?" Louis gasped.

Long after Bob had gone back to his own home, Louis continued what he and his family called "Skeltery." He almost lived inside his model theater. He grew very clever at taking every part and acting as stage manager as well. At last Mr. Smith had to admit sadly that Louis had bought every one of the plays Mr. Skelt had published.

"Then I shall make my own," Louis said.

Mr. Smith sighed. He saw no profit in that.

Louis drew new scenes and characters on cardboard. Ali Baba and all Forty Thieves. Sinbad the Sailor carrying the Old Man of the Sea on his back. The giant roc flying with an elephant clutched in its claws. He colored them all and cut them out. He wrote parts for his characters and spoke them.

By that time Louis was reading every interesting book he could set hands on. He was lucky, for nobody ever told him a book was "too old for him." Most of his father's library looked dull or difficult—books about engineering or religion, or books written in Latin. But among them on the shelves Louis found stories by Sir Walter Scott.

There was nothing dull about those tales. If they were difficult, Louis never knew it. The people in them were the sort he most wanted to meet—knights and pirates, King Robert the Bruce and the Lord of the Isles. Louis read the stories, and he turned them into plays.

Nearly every evening after tea, he gave a play for his family and the servants and any guests who might happen in. When a new play was finished, Donal, the boot boy, always

Louis found stories by Sir Walter Scott

alled out, "Master Lou, give us the *Inchcape Bell* noo. I like well the de'il ringing for that Rover."

Louis never needed a second invitation to recite those stirring lines. The household at Heriot Row got to know them by heart. So did all their friends. So did Grandfather Balfour and Aunt Jane and the cousins at Colinton. So did Mr. Henderson at the little school Louis attended when he was well enough.

"Smout, would you like to visit the lighthouse your grandfather built on Inchcape Rock?" Mr. Stevenson asked Louis one day. "You're ten years old now—and I was ten when I first made a tour of inspection with my father. Though there weren't as many lighthouses in those days to inspect."

"I'd like it fine, Papa. When can we start?"

"The day after tomorrow. Get Cummie to lay out your woolens. It's apt to be chilly on the North Sea in September."

Cummie worried about Louis' weak chest. "And what will you do, Master Lou," she ended, "if you come over seasick and me not there to tend you?"

Louis felt insulted. "Why, Cummie, I *never* get seasick!"

[*43*]

"How would you know that when you'v
not been to sea yet?"

Mr. Stevenson answered for Louis. "H
knows well enough, Cummie. Lighthous
Stevensons do not get seasick."

Louis felt very important when the
boarded the little steamer *Pharos*. He wante
to see everything from engine room to pilo
house. He strode the deck with a very nautica
roll. He thrilled to the shrill whistle whicl
announced their departure. He leaned fa
over the rail to watch a paddle wheel churn
ing up creamy water as the *Pharos* set ou
down the Firth of Forth to the North Sea

Where the firth opened into the wide gra
sea, Louis saw his first beacon towering o
the Isle of May.

"When your grandfather started workin
with the Board of Northern Lights, this wa
the only point lighted on the whole Scottis
coast," Mr. Stevenson told him. "An ope
coal fire blazed on the tower."

"That must have looked fine," said Louis

"No doubt it did, but it was not enough
Seamen all over the world heard that Scottis
coasts were to be avoided after dark. O
course steamboats are a new thing, and you
grandfather traveled by sloop. He did some o

his first work in the very camps where wreckers used to show lights to lure ships to destruction on the rocks."

Louis found this as good as a story by Sir Walter Scott. He wished Grandfather Stevenson were still alive to tell him all about it.

"I think I'll write a tale about a wrecker," he announced.

"You do that, Smout." But Mr. Stevenson really thought it more important for Louis to learn about the family profession. "The Board first planned only four new lights," he said, "but twenty towers rose in your grandfather's day. There was no stopping him."

"There's been no stopping your father or your uncles either, young man," declared the mate, who came along the deck to have a word with Mr. Stevenson. "Because of them, Scotland stands foremost among nations for her coastal beacons."

Louis drew himself up proudly, every inch a Lighthouse Stevenson.

Whenever the *Pharos* anchored that first wonderful day, Louis was quick as a monkey to clamber down into the captain's gig. At lighthouse points and islands, keepers welcomed him as if it were perfectly natural that he should be making an inspection tour.

By the time the captain put his ship's nose straight out into the North Sea, the afternoon was gray and squally. When Mr. Stevenson came out of the cabin where he had been writing reports, he did not have to look for Louis. Familiar, ringing words guided him to the pilot house.

> " '. . . *as if with the Inchcape Bell*
> *The devil below was ringing his knell.'*

"And then my grandfather came and built

Bell Rock Lighthouse so ships don't get wrecked there any more."

"That he did." The grizzled skipper smiled down at the youngest Lighthouse Stevenson, whose hand was on the wheel alongside his own. "I was but a lad then—fifty years ago—but I mind it well. And I took your Uncle Alan out to build Skerryvore Lighthouse on the west coast—and your father and your Uncle David when they were old enough to work with him.

"It took six years to build that hundred
and-thirty-foot tower, and men risked death
every day there. When you decide where
you're going to build your first tower, just le
me know. I'll take you there."

"Papa, I can hardly wait to see Skerryvore!" Louis said as his father came up. "It's
the greatest lighthouse ever built on offshore
reefs, isn't it?"

"That may be, Smout," his father said.
"But remember, we could not have done it
if your grandfather hadn't built Bell Rock

light first. He worked out the construction problems. We used his experience."

"A mighty wicked place, Inchcape Rock," the captain told Louis. "It only shows at low water. Men could only work four hours at a stretch, and then be rowed back to the sloop *Smeaton*. My father was a mason on that job, and he told me that once the *Smeaton* slipped her mooring in a stiff wind. She wasn't even in sight when the tide began running in round the men."

Louis shivered, thinking about the marooned workmen. "Were they all saved?"

"Aye, but it was a near thing. The water came to my dad's waist before he was taken off. They had fish for supper that night. He said he was thankful to be eating it after coming so close to being a supper for fish."

Mr. Stevenson laughed. Then he pointed. "Look, Smout, a little northeast there, and you'll catch your first glimpse of Bell Rock."

Louis saw the tower loom through the drizzle. Then, as if nature were celebrating his first visit, the rain stopped suddenly. By the time the *Pharos* dropped anchor, the sun had turned the sea to a golden shimmer.

The tide was high, and waves slapped the stone tower. From the gig, it seemed to Louis

that it rose almost to the clouds. And the iro
ladder up its side looked frail as a spiderwel
He felt peculiar in his stomach.

"Up you go!" said his father.

Louis tried not to think about the heigh
He felt as if he had been climbing for an hou
when he happened to glance down. Far, fa
below, waves danced and glittered.

Horribly giddy, he shut his eyes and clung
to an iron rung. He was sure he could never
take another step.

"Remember you're a Lighthouse Steven
son, Smout." That was his father's voice just
below him.

Louis gulped. He began to climb again,
still without daring to open his eyes. At last,
strong hands pulled him through a door in
the side of the tower.

"Inspectors come in smaller sizes this
year," said a voice.

Louis opened his eyes to find the keeper
smiling at him. The floor of the entry seemed
to sway under his feet. But he did not mean
to let a lighthouse keeper know that he had
been frightened. "I am Robert Louis Stevenson," he announced.

"You're a Stevenson right enough," the

keeper agreed. "And I'll be bound there's little you miss in your inspection."

They went up a winding staircase into one round room on top of another. An oil room with enormous tanks of whale oil. A storeroom for supplies. The keeper's bedroom and then his living room, as snug and tidy as a ship's cabin. There the keeper brought an album to show Louis. "Here, read what Sir Walter Scott wrote about your grandfather."

"Sir Walter Scott wrote about *my* grandfather?"

"Didn't you know that, Smout?" his father asked. "They were good friends. On an inspection trip like this one, Sir Walter made notes for two of his books that you know— *The Pirate* and *Lord of the Isles.*"

"A fine companion," Sir Walter had called Robert Stevenson in the album. Louis kept thinking about it when they inspected the room where lamps were polished and filled.

The sun was just setting when they reached the great lantern with its glittering prisms. The keeper showed Louis how shutters provided the changing topaz and ruby lights. "Your father invented this revolving light, and I daresay it will be used as long as there are lighthouses. Now you can be the man to light Bell Rock tonight."

Touching wick after wick in the lantern into flame flowers, Louis felt as magical as Leerie. It was wonderful to make a light shine on dark waters to keep seamen safe.

When his father and the keeper went back down the winding staircase, Louis stayed for a while beside the lantern. He felt very happy. He was going to sleep on shipboard, and the tour would last for days and days. Some day *he* would be Engineer to the Board of Northern Lights.

He meant to do more than that, for he was going to be an author as well. His grandfather wrote books, but they were only about building lighthouses and bridges. *He* was going to write stories like Sir Walter Scott.

The sea was almost dark now except for a bright path that Bell Rock Light threw across the water. By that gleam, Louis saw a schooner under full sail, beating into the Firth of Tay from the North Sea. She was safe because her skipper had Bell Rock Light to guide him. Louis felt very proud of that. Then another thought occurred to him.

"I wonder if she's ever flown the Jolly Roger," he said to himself.

CHAPTER SIX
The Lantern Bearers

Y OU'LL be back tonight?" Louis asked.
"It's the dark of the moon."

"Sure to be," his friend Garry answered.
"It's beastly having to visit relatives."

Garry jumped into the carriage with his
mother and sisters, and it clattered away.
Louis called Coolin to go to the beach. He
did not agree that it was beastly to visit relatives.

His grandfather Balfour had died. A new
minister and a new family lived in Colinton
Manse. No longer did cousins from all over
the British Empire come there to be moth-
ered by Aunt Jane.

The only signs the cousins had left at
Colinton Manse were shot holes peppering
the strong wooden gates. Louis and the others
had used the gates as a target.

Louis had been dreadfully lonely when th
Stevensons first came to spend summer holi
days at North Berwick. He was a bit happie
now that he had found enough friends to star
a secret society. He did wish, though, that hi
club had a few more members. Perhaps nex
season, Willie and Henrietta could visit, o
Bob and his sister Katherine.

Half an hour later, Louis was nearly asleep
in the sun on top of Black Rock that rose like
an Alp out of the sand. Beside him Coolir
dreamed with twitching paws and excited
little yips.

Suddenly a hat appeared in front of Louis
eyes and stayed motionless. He wriggled
across to peer over the edge of the crag into
the strained face of another boy. The newcomer had put his wrong foot foremost and
could get no farther. He was in real danger.

Louis stretched his long, skinny arm to
grasp the boy's wrist. "Hold tight!" he com-
manded. "Now change your footing. Back,
Coolin!" He pushed a foot backward to dis-
courage Coolin's efforts to be helpful.

"Ready now?" he asked the boy. "All right.
One—two—three—UP!"

At twelve, Louis was almost as thin as a
skeleton, but he had an astonishingly strong

rip. The bigger boy was pulled to safety.

"Whew, that was a close squeak!" He gave a huge sigh of relief. "I'm glad you were here! When I saw you climbing, I took you for my cousin, so I followed. We only arrived yesterday, and I didn't want Jamie stealing a march on me. I am James Macrae and so is my cousin, so we call him Jamie."

"I know all about that," Louis laughed. "I have heaps of cousins named Lewis, so we have to call them after the places where they were born. Then I've got a cousin Robert that we call Bob. I was named for both grandfathers, so I am Robert Louis. But everybody calls me Lou. If that's your cousin coming along the strand we'd better go down and meet him. This climb is tricky till you get used to it."

"Don't I know it, just!" James Macrae said.

Both Macraes found Louis full of strange tales and ideas. In the past two years he had visited Germany and Switzerland and Italy and France with his mother. He didn't tell the boys the reason for all that traveling—trying to find a climate where he would have fewer winter coughs. Instead, he had an exciting new game to introduce to them.

"Let's go crusoing," he proposed.

[55]

They had never heard the word *crusoing*
but they had read *Robinson Crusoe,* so the
could guess what Louis meant. The thre
boys and Coolin followed the falling tide ou
to a little island of rippled sand.

"Now we're marooned on a desert island,"
Louis announced. "What can we eat?" Whe
he came up with such an idea, it was mor
than make-believe to Louis. For the tim
being, he *was* marooned and starving.

"Catch a goat and cook it?" suggeste
James.

"When you've just been shipwrecked
you're too exhausted to catch anything a
first," Louis declared. "And you don't hav
a fire for cooking. I think it'll have to b

something like shrimps—and eat them raw!

Silvery wrigglers darted about in a clear sea pool. The boys caught some in their hands, but somehow the shrimp did not look tempting.

"No worse than raw oysters," Louis pointed out. "People eat them."

His companions were doubtful. "How do you begin, Lou?"

Louis felt peculiar, too, but he wouldn't admit it. "Best start with the head," he decided. "That will kill them at once."

The Macraes followed Louis' order just as his cousins had done. The shrimps were not quite as bad as they had feared.

"Very nutritious," Jamie said gravely. "My hunger is satisfied."

"Mine, too." Louis agreed that a single shrimp was a full meal for a starving man. Eating it had made him feel like a cannibal.

But the experiment had proved to Louis that these new boys were worthy to join his secret society. They could leave their villa to night without any grownups finding out, they promised. And luckily, they happened to have the equipment club members needed.

The September night was black when muffled figures crept out of one house after

nother. Louis was first, soon joined by the
Macrae cousins. Then other night-shrouded
figures arrived until a small, silent procession
was making its way to the harbor.

"Have you got your lantern?" Louis whispered to each newcomer.

"Yes." The answer came out of the dark,
but not a glimmer was seen. That was the
club's first rule.

Not until they had clambered down into
the scaly hold of a fishing smack was their secret revealed. Coats were unbuttoned then.
Slides were slipped back so that light showed
the tin bull's-eye lantern fastened to each
boyish middle by a cricket belt. A reek of
roasting tinware was added to the high smell
of bilgewater and seaweed.

Of course the club had been Louis' idea.
He had known how exciting it would be to
walk through the village, dark as the night
and hidden from every eye. And all the time
—quite unsuspected—they carried lighted
lanterns.

"Fellow Lantern Bearers," Louis opened
the meeting. "Tonight we have two new
members—James Macrae and Jamie Macrae.
Once again we have safely reached our desti-
nation, undetected, unsuspected, un—er—"

Muffled figures crept out of one house after another

" 'Ungry?" suggested a fat boy. "You ought o be, Lou. You're so skinny you have to tand twice in the same place to throw a hadow."

Pockets were turned out to produce contributions. Share and share alike, Louis handed out biscuits, toffee, a link of sausage, and some odd snippets of cheese while the air hickened with lantern smoke. Then a sudden noise overhead froze every movement.

"Button up!" Louis whispered. Overcoats were fastened, and not a gleam showed. In he thick, smelly dark every ear was strained. They heard a scrabbling at the hatch. This time it was followed by a little whine.

"It's Coolin! Don't show your lanterns till I get him." Cautiously, Louis lifted the hatch cover and reached for his dog. "He's brought something. It's slippery. Maybe an eel."

Presently the lanterns showed Coolin very pleased with himself for tracking his master. They also showed his contribution to the party—a leg of mutton.

"Coolin's an awful thief," Louis told the others. "Cook roasted that mutton so we could have it cold for a picnic tomorrow."

"I suppose you have to take it home." The fat boy sounded discouraged.

Louis inspected the meat. It was dusty. Toothmarks showed that Coolin had paused for a slight snack along the way. "I don't think Cook would really want it this way," he decided. "We're starving men saved by our faithful hound."

The Lantern Bearers made a fine supper. The faithful hound gnawed the bone.

"How about a ghost story, Lou?" Garry asked after they were all well stuffed with food and well smoked by their lanterns.

"Not tonight, men. We've got work ahead." From pockets and other hiding places among his garments, Louis drew forth length after length of cloth. "I've been painting these all week," he said. Then he issued instructions. "Remember," he ended. "Not a sound. And not a light."

Shadowy figures soon stole from the hold of the fishing smack. And next morning the population of North Berwick got a real surprise. Their herring fleet had turned into a pirate fleet overnight. Every fishing smack in the harbor was flying the Jolly Roger. From every mainmast, a white flag with black skull and crossbones snapped in the wind.

CHAPTER SEVEN
Hell, Heaven, and Purgatory

THE arrival of the Edinburgh train was a big event in Peebles. On a sunny August day every boy in town was watching for it. Louis was allowed through the gate because he was meeting two of his cousins.

During his months at Burgh School, Louis had found Peebles a pleasant enough town. Now that Bob would be sharing his vacation, everything good about it loomed twice as bright. Louis felt like dancing a Highland fling on the platform, but that would look silly in a boy nearly fifteen.

The train rushed in, chuffing and ringing its big brass bell. The first passenger off was Bob Stevenson.

"You keep getting taller, Lou," was his

greeting. "But you don't grow any wider. I
you weren't set on a career as a Lighthous
Stevenson, you could hire out as a scarecrow."

"You shouldn't tease him," Bob's siste
Katherine protested as soon as she coul
make herself heard above a screech of escap
ing steam. "Poor Lou can't help being thin a
a stork."

Louis laughed. "I'd as soon be a scarecrov
as a stork, Kat. Bob's teasing never bother
me. Let Donal take your luggage along in the
cart and we'll walk. I have places to show you
And a surprise when we get home."

Donal was the freckle-faced boot boy now
promoted to groom. He grinned at Bob as an
old friend. "You've grown some yourself
Master Bob. Now you're here, I expect we'll
see some Skeltery. How about you and Master
Lou giving us the *Inchcape Bell* tonight?"

"They'll be busy this evening," Louis told
Donal. "I want them to help me put tunes to
The Baneful Potato. I can manage rhymes,
but the music stops me. And what's an opera
without music?"

"An opera about a potato?" Katherine
asked, as she climbed into the station cart.

"Well, it's a comic opera—I hope. Two of
my characters are 'Dig-him-up-o, the gar-

[*64*]

lener,' and 'Seek-him-out-o, the policeman.'
But you'll hear it . . ."

Louis drove his cousins home by a round-
about way to show Bob his favorite haunts.

"That Castle on the north bank of the
river," he said, "has a tower dating back to
King Robert the Bruce. About eight hundred years before Bruce, King Arthur is sup-
posed to have fought a battle here—in the
year 530. And hundreds of years before that,
the Romans—"

"The same old Lou," Bob interrupted
with a laugh. "Trust you to learn all the history of the place!"

"I do like history," Louis admitted. "Especially with lots of battles. The headmaster
at Burgh School likes history, too. He told
Mother and Father I was the most intelligent
and best-informed boy in his experience."

Louis was grinning impishly, and his cousins saw the joke. "Good thing history is his
pet subject and not mathematics," Bob commented.

"And has he ever seen your spelling?"
Katherine put in. "Did his compliment fool
Uncle Tom and Aunt Maggie?"

"I don't think so, really. I heard Mother
say she thought my schoolmasters would al-

ways rather talk to me than teach me. Guess what I learned from my French master when we were at Mentone last winter—card tricks!"

"I wager you did better at them than at French grammar," Bob said.

The house the Stevensons had leased for the summer was a big, sprawling place where generations of children had played. Louis led his cousins round the side to a cobbled stable-yard. The upper panels were all open in a row of doors. Out of each opening poked an inquisitive nose, and big eyes rolled to watch their approach.

First there was the pair of dappled grays that always looked so smart with the family carriage. Then the elderly horse Donal had just unharnessed from the station cart. Beyond these were three ponies. Not stocky little Shetland ponies, but high-spirited ones almost as tall as the horses.

"This is my Purgatory," Louis introduced the first. "Isn't he a beauty?" Purgatory bobbed his head and whinnied at the compliment.

"You *are* lucky, Lou," Katherine said. "I wish I had a pony."

"You do have for the summer. That is the

surprise. Father hired these two for you from the man who raised Purgatory. Your little mare, Kat, is a perfect angel, and her name is Heaven. And here's black Hell waiting for you, Bob."

Katherine forgot about being ladylike. She whooped as loudly as Bob.

"How did they come by those names?" Bob asked.

"I don't know why they called my bay Purgatory," Louis said. "But the other two had ordinary names till I decided they ought to match Purgatory. You needn't worry—they know their new names all right now."

Katherine rubbed the white blaze on Heaven's chestnut nose. She sighed with satisfaction. "This is going to be a perfect holiday," she declared.

A perfect holiday is exactly what the next weeks were.

Louis and his cousins explored the castle and several other interesting places. For long golden days all three found the Tweed the most perfect of rivers. Ferny banks on which to eat enormous picnic lunches that Cook and Cummie packed for them. Dark brown pools to swim in. Rapids to provide a spice of danger when the boys shot them in a tippy boat. One stretch of the stream was shallow enough to ford on horseback.

It was past noon when they set out one day. The morning had followed an old rule—rain before seven, clear before eleven. They splashed through the river under a sky scoured of clouds and polished by wind to a dazzling blue. When they pulled up their ponies on the far bank to wait for Coolin, a blackbird was whistling among new-washed leaves. Bob whistled an answering call.

"This is the kind of day when I want to do nothing except look and listen," Katherine said.

Louis felt that way, too. At least he did while Coolin shook himself after his swim and then rolled in sun-warmed bracken to dry off. But Louis had stored up too much energy all morning to be lazy very long.

"Let's have a race!" he proposed.

He soon lined his cousins up on the Queen's Highway. Then he set the rules. "I'll shout, 'Get set—GO!' and we'll race as far as that big beech tree at the bend in the road. Whoever reaches that point first wins the dash. But the important thing is to find out how much stamina our mounts have. So we'll go on galloping till we reach the Red Lion Inn."

"Where is that?" Katherine wanted to

know. "I've never been along here, and I think you're up to something."

"I'm not taking a short-cut," Louis promised. "The Red Lion is two miles past the bend, and we'll stick to the highway all the way. Agreed?"

"I suppose so," Bob said, watching his cousin. He couldn't remember when that mischievous glint in the eye hadn't meant Louis was up to some deviltry.

"All right then. Now . . . Get set! GO!"

The three ponies started fair, thudding along the highway. Coolin brought up the rear, doing his best to overtake the riders. But he was getting a little fat and wasted a good deal of breath in excited yelps.

Excitement mounted as they neared the beech tree. Louis and Bob were racing practically neck and neck.

"Oh, Hell wins, I say!" Louis yelled. After a quick glance back, he called to Katherine. "Don't hold Heaven in, Kat!"

An instant later he pulled ahead. "Purgatory will beat you both!"

And Purgatory did nose past Hell while Heaven trailed behind.

There was no pause at the beech tree. Round the bend, Bob saw that he and Katherine had been quite right in suspecting Louis. Directly before them was a toll gate. If Louis could get through the bars before the keeper came out of his cottage, he'd gain time to let him reach the Red Lion first.

"I'm coming right through with you!" Bob shouted to Louis. "Come on, Hell. Gallop like the devil!"

"We're moss-troopers storming the barricades!" Louis' teeth gleamed in a grin as he spurred his pony. Together the two boys thundered through the toll bars before the old keeper could stop them. But he was out in time to vent his fury upon Katherine and Heaven and Coolin.

[*71*]

Katherine had very winning manners. She needed them and all her pocket money for tolls before the angry man would let her ride after the boys.

Louis and Bob were walking their ponies to cool them when she and Coolin reached the Red Lion. Louis was telling Bob about a story he was writing.

"I've called it *The Wreckers,* and it begins with two men on the beach at North Berwick. They're by the foot of Black Rock, but I've changed its name to Spyglasse Hill. The older man wears a blue coat with tarnished gold lace, and he's got a red nose and grizzled hair. The other fellow could be taken for a fisherman except that he has a pistol sticking out of each pocket in his pea jacket. They're going to a wreck where a sailor clings—"

Katherine was too indignant to mind interrupting a story. "You boys owe me toll money," she announced, pulling up Heaven.

But once Louis was well started on a story, you couldn't stop him with a small matter like that. It was on another August afternoon two years later, and in quite another place, that Katherine reminded them again of that debt.

CHAPTER EIGHT

A Day to Remember

SUNLIGHT gilded a stone cottage set snugly into a green fold of the Pentland Hills. It warmed the tall boy carving his initials into the bark of a tree in the garden.

R. L. S. He cut each letter carefully while his terrier watched with his head cocked. Coolin might be getting a bit elderly, but he had never lost his puppyish interest in anything Louis was doing.

"R. L. S. Very nice monogram." Bob remarked. "Is it to become famous?"

Louis laughed, and Coolin wagged.

Bob and Katherine sat on the ground, idly chewing grass stems, while they watched Louis add the date, 1867, the year the Stevensons had moved to Swanston Cottage.

Mr. Stevenson had taken the house in the hope that they could live there every year from March through October. That would cut short his lonely winters at Heriot Row when Louis and his mother had to go to the south of France. Swanston was only half an hour from Edinburgh, but no one would have guessed that it was not in the very heart of the country. Even in the cold months, the air was milder and not smoky.

Louis had lost no time in making friends with farmhands and with John Todd, called the Roaring Shepherd because of his tremendous voice. It was roaring that first caused

Louis to meet Todd. Walking up the hill with Coolin, he had been stopped in his tracks by a wrathful bellow. "Coom awa oot amang those sheep. Hae ye no the sense to keep your dog from chasing them?"

Louis whistled Coolin back. He hurried to apologize to the shepherd. "I'm sorry. I was thinking, and I didn't notice."

"Thinking's no reason for behaving like a daftie," John Todd said.

Louis admitted he was right, and they soon became fast friends. Coolin learned to walk sedately among sheep instead of trying to play tag with the silly creatures. Louis loved the hills and spent hours picking out ancient battlefields in them, seeing where his countrymen had made their history.

Katherine's mind turned to history today, too, but it was more recent history. "This is a very do-you-remember sort of day," she said when Louis pocketed his knife and flopped down on the grass with them. "I keep thinking of all the holidays we three have shared."

"So do I," her brother said. "Actually I was remembering the number of times Lou has come close to drowning me. When we raced our model boats and he insisted on a finish line a mile out at sea. And the raft he

built on the river Tweed that he *said* wa
perfectly safe for us both."

"You shouldn't complain!" Katherine said
with a laugh. "I was the one carried through
the air by that enormous kite you two made."

"You flew like a swan at sunrise," Louis
told her. "I envied you."

"Well, I landed like a sack of potatoes."
Katherine sat up straight. "Hah! I've just
remembered. You two owe me money—lots
of money with two years' interest added."

"Whatever for?" her brother asked.

But Louis knew at once. "Hell, Heaven
and Purgatory!"

"That's it. It was only by pure luck I had
enough money to pay those tolls."

"But we treated you to a jolly good tea at
the Red Lion," Louis defended himself

"I sometimes wonder what your ideas of
fun will lead you into when you begin building lighthouses, Lou," Bob commented
"Collapsible spiral staircases? Roman candles
shooting out of the tower?"

"No, you don't play pranks with the safety
of ships and seamen." It was a Lighthouse
Stevenson speaking now. "My towers will be
sound and solid. That is, if I ever do become
an engineer at all."

Now that he was older, Louis realized how much he did not know. Illness had too often kept him out of school. Because of his travels he was good at languages—French, German, and Italian. And when he was interested in a subject, he worked hard at it. But he was apt to be wild or absent-minded in classes that had nothing to do with history or literature. He dreaded the day when his father would find out how bad he was in mathematics.

"But you have been accepted at the University, haven't you, Lou?" Katherine asked her cousin.

"Oh, yes. I'm a student of Edinburgh University now—at least till they find me out. There are even professors who encourage me to write."

"As if you ever needed encouragement for that!" Bob exploded. "Think of all the magazines you were forever starting, with you doing all the writing for them."

"I'll never forget the *Schoolboys' Magazine*," Katherine put in. "You broke off a story, Lou, with your hero hidden in a boiler under which somebody had lighted a fire. It scared me into nightmares."

"And what became of *The Wreckers?*" Bob asked.

"That story was so bad I threw away every
thing except the title," Louis admitted. "Bu
if you two have to bring up those early howl
ers, you might at least mention *The Pentlan*
Rising."

Louis couldn't help being a little proud o
that story about the history of these very hills
He had written it when he was barely sixteen
His father had been impressed enough to pa
for having a few hundred copies printed
"My first book," Louis said.

"Well, it won't be your last, Lou." Bol
declared. "It would take more than being ar
engineer to stop you from writing."

"But it will stop me from writing as much
as I want. After all, you ought to become an
engineer too, Bob. You're as much a Light
house Stevenson as I am."

"Not for me," Bob declared. "I'm going to
Cambridge University and then off to Paris
to paint pictures. It's what I *have* to do."

And that was the way Louis felt about writing. It was what he *had* to do.

When Cummie called them to tea, Louis
let his cousins go ahead. He went back to the
tree where he had cut his initials.

"I don't see how I can ever do it, Coolin,"
he told his dog. He was remembering all the

stories he had written and torn up because they were not what he thought they ought to be. "It would take me all my life to become a really *good* writer. How can I build light-houses as well?"

He stared moodily at his carving. R. L. S. 1867.

Would that monogram ever be famous, as Bob suggested and as he hoped? And if it should be famous some day, how would it read?

R. L. S. Builder of Lighthouses or *R. L. S. Teller of Tales?*

CHAPTER NINE

Meeting the Fish at Home

LOUIS' friends at Edinburgh University would never have recognized him when he came out of his lodging in the town of Wick. Layer upon layer of heavy woolen underwear made him look ready to bulge out of the greatcoat that usually flapped round his thin shanks. They slowed his lope to a fat man's waddle. He wore a nightcap on the head he bent against the biting salt wind from the North Sea.

After a year at the University, his father decided it was time for Louis to learn the practical side of engineering. So he was spending his vacation in storm-beaten Wick.

Close to Scotland's northeast corner, there were neither trees nor gardens here. Cliffs ose like pillars out of crashing surf. The wind felt as if it blew straight from the North Pole as Louis beat his way down the High Street.

At the harbor, an unfinished breakwater reared out of the waves like a dark reef. Louis crossed the wooden staging which led to the breakwater with nothing beneath him but the turbulent rise and fall of the sea.

Three men waited for him on a platform of loose planks with a diving suit and helmet at their feet. Louis was surprised that his friend, the diver Bob Bain, was not among them.

"Bain told us to expect you." The oldest man had a worried look. "He's a scamp to have a hand in this. I don't know what your father would say. But we've got the equipment ready—if you're still of a mind to go on."

"That I am!" Louis told him. "This is my reward for a year of dull lectures at the University. I'm taking all the fun I can."

The men found Louis' idea of fun rather peculiar. To them diving was dangerous work. By the time they had helped him into the diving suit and hung twenty-pound lead weights on his legs and back, Louis began to

[*81*]

wonder if they might not be right. When two
men lifted the helmet, he didn't know if he
would be able to stand up under it. The third
man stepped over to an air mill.

"You're sure that machine will keep on
pumping air to me?" Louis hoped it sounded
like a joke, and not as shaky as he felt.

"You'll know soon enough if it doesn't!"
came the grim reply. Then the man added
more cheerfully, "We'll have two pumps
working. They've never both broken down at
the same time yet. We'd not want to lose a
Stevenson—not if we're to go on working for
your father."

"You'll have a line, remember," said another man, who was helping ease the helmet
over Louis' head. "One tug when you're
ready to surface. If you run into trouble, give
three sharp tugs, and we'll haul you up fast."

The oldest man screwed down the visor.
The one at the pump began to turn the handle. Louis felt a moment's panic before the
comforting whistle of air came through the
tube. It was like being deaf and dumb, standing beside people he couldn't talk to.

The assistants motioned him toward the
ladder. Crushed almost double under the
weight of the helmet, Louis felt clumsily for

each rung with lead-encased feet. Twenty rungs down, twilight fell though it was mid-morning. Over his head, a low green heaven was shot through with yeasty white swirls. Thirty rungs down, he stepped off onto the foundation of the breakwater.

In this new world, helmet and lead weights were no longer heavy. Louis felt light and giddy. He took a dizzy joy in snatching at fish darting past as swift as humming birds. He laughed uproariously when a fat grandfather fish peered short-sightedly in at him through the visor. It looked so much like an absent-minded professor.

"Oh, no, my fine finny friend." He waved the creature aside. "If you must lecture, find yourself a school of fish."

Suddenly the big fish swerved and vanished, going, perhaps, in search of his school. Louis felt like following when he saw a monster with a glass snout approaching. Then he laughed when he recognized Bob Bain's grinning face. Only then did he remember that a fourth man up on the opposite side of the staging had been turning an air pump handle all the time Louis was putting on his heavy diving suit.

"So you went down first to make sure I

wasn't running off with your gear?" Louis
asked, forgetting that Bain could not hear.

Bain led Louis to where the work on the
breakwater had been going on. The wall of

stone blocks was like an unfinished rampart built by some undersea giant. Bain motioned him to jump to the top of a rock that towered above his head.

Bain liked a joke, but Louis had no intention of making a fool of himself trying to carry out such an order. In upper air without clumsy gear, he might have been able to scramble to the top of that stone block. But he could never have jumped to the top. Bain kept on motioning, but Louis only grinned back. Just to prove the absurdity of the notion, he bent his knees and gave a small spring.

Then he gasped. He was soaring like a bird, with Bain rising beside him. Louis would have gone far beyond the boulder's flat top if Bain had not laid a strong arm across his shoulders. Even then, his heels kept on rising till he was upside down. Bain had to haul him in, hand over hand, and set him on his feet, swaying in the invisible sea swell.

"So," Louis told himself ruefully, "water *is* buoyant as the textbooks say. You'd think I might have remembered."

Louis was alone for a bit while Bain was doing some piece of undersea work. He was thoroughly enjoying this different world, but he realized that, left to himself, he wouldn't have the foggiest idea which way to turn to find the ladder.

He had his lifeline, of course. Three tugs would get him hauled up to the surface in short order. But wouldn't he hate having to admit that the only emergency was that he was lost!

Once this idea had occurred to him, it stuck in his mind. He kept remembering Bain's love of practical jokes. So he was greatly relieved when the diver finally reappeared and led him back to the ladder. A moment later he was up in a world of gray sea, gray sky, and whistling wind.

The day's excitement did not end with his diving adventure. That afternoon Louis was overseeing the unloading of planks from a scow when he was startled by a shout.

"Help needed! Angus has gone over!"

Louis sprinted to the edge of the staging. He saw Angus in the water, clutching for a line that had been tossed to him.

"Hold on!" someone yelled. "We're away for a skiff to pick you up."

"I cannot do it!" Angus' voice reached Louis above the sound of the wind. Angus was not a young man, and a heavy swell ran in that icy sea. Louis saw that he was near exhaustion, holding himself by the rope.

"Lower a plank here, men!" he shouted. Nobody heard in the excitement, but Louis managed to grab Bob Bain by the arm. Together they hauled a plank across the staging and passed a rope around it. But more men were needed to lower it.

Angus was close to drowning, and all the men had gone for the skiff. Angry because this seemed so stupid, Louis and Bob struggled with the life-saving plank. Finally it was on its way down. But by then the need for it was past. The boat arrived, and Angus was hauled aboard, more dead than alive.

With the danger over, everybody admitted that Louis' plan for rescuing Angus would have been best. They felt sheepish about being so slow to see it. Angus was taken ashore, but the accident did not stop the work. Neither did the rain that settled in for the rest of the day. Louis was drenched when he went in to supper.

"This is still the best part of being an engineer!" he told himself while changing into dry clothes.

He did enjoy it. Friendship with men whose lives were ruled by tides and winds

Sitting on the thwart of a tossing boat, sharing the danger of crashing waves and roaring skerry. Even working till his hands were blistered. Ships and seas and perilous reefs were the stuff of life. But to leave them and go back to a stuffy office where he must work with compass, rule, and figures—that was not for him!

Louis would always rather be chilled and in danger than warm and dead-alive in a comfortable office. At his desk, he was forever discovering something he had not measured. Or if he had measured it, he had not made a note of it. Or if he had noted the figures, he could not find them again. Or else they were wrong from the start.

It might suit other Lighthouse Stevensons, but it was not Louis' recipe for a happy life. Even the outdoor part did not leave him time enough for his main interest. But he might snatch an hour or two now if he could stay awake.

Louis lit a second candle on the rough table he had brought to his attic room for a desk. Everyone else in the house had gone to bed. Soon the only noise was his pen scratching across the paper.

With his left hand, he reached over and

shut the notebook of mathematical problem
he ought to study. Even if he left it open, h
wouldn't learn much from the figures. Th

last time he had tried studying it, he had only
ended by scribbling some lines in the mar-
gin:

> *"My candle goes not out by night,*
> *And many a time*
> *I work into the morning light*
> *To find a rhyme."*

[*90*]

CHAPTER TEN

A Promise and New Hope

AN APPLEWOOD fire crackled on the hearth at Swanston Cottage. On the eighth of April, its warmth was welcome in spite of all the sunshine outdoors. Firelight twinkled on Mrs. Stevenson's silver thimble as she embroidered crimson silks into a pattern of roses. Cummie was darning one of Louis' stockings. Everything in the room looked cozy and cheerful—except Louis. He sat by the fire, holding a novel by Sir Walter Scott. His eyes scanned a page, but saw no words. At last, closing his book, he rose from his chair.

"I *cannot* do it!" His voice was quite desperate when he broke a long silence. He kicked at the burning logs. They tumbled in a shower of sparks.

His mother and Cummie looked at each

other, but they did not speak. They both knew what troubled him, but neither had any idea what to do about it. Cummie wished her Master Lou was still a child to comfort with a story. But this year he would be twenty-one years old.

Louis' words had startled himself. That was what old Angus said when he expected to drown. And Louis thought Angus had sounded calmer than he did.

"I'm sorry to be such poor company," he told his mother and Cummie. "I'll go let the wind blow the cobwebs out of my head. As our Roaring Shepherd, John Todd, has often told me, thinking is no reason for behaving like a daftie. Father is out walking on the hill, isn't he? I think I'll join him."

He left the house. At the end of the garden, he stopped at a small mound. Louis touched the stone over it as if he were patting the little dog he had buried there two years ago. He had composed the words for that stone:

> "To Coolin, the gentle and friendly, who in a green old age, by some unhappy chance, met his death at the place where three roads meet, where the hunters are wont to gather. This stone has been set up to his memory by his sorrowing friends.
> *1869.* R. L. S.

R. L. S. The initials Coolin had watched him carve on the tree near by. Louis did not look at them today. He felt himself a failure, and he did not want to be reminded of his high hopes of making that monogram famous.

Away on the top of Halkerside, he could see his father, looking no larger than a walking doll. Louis set off after him. He did not pause to watch the spring lambs kicking up their heels among their sedate mothers. He did not stop for one of his long talks with their shepherd.

When he had almost caught up to Mr. Stevenson, he was tempted to turn back. He stopped by a tiny pool, overhung by a rock, where he loved to sit and write verses. It was like a little cave, and he was hidden there. He could put off that talk he dreaded for yet another day.

It would never be easy to say what he had to say to his father. He admired Thomas Stevenson more than any other man. He loved him dearly. Yet he was going to bring his father the bitterest disappointment of his life But perhaps he wouldn't do it quite yet.

Louis took a deep breath. Putting off something bad did not change it in the end. It

would be better to go on and get it over. He
came out from the rock and whistled—a spe
cial whistle he and his father had often used
Mr. Stevenson looked back, and stopped.

"This is a pleasure, son," he said when
Louis joined him. "It has been too long since
we walked together."

"It—it won't be a pleasure, I'm afraid."
Louis tried to keep his voice from breaking.

"Father, I've got to talk to you. It would be dishonest not to speak frankly. The long and the short of it is I want to give up studying engineering. I shall never be a Lighthouse Stevenson, and it is foolish for either of us to expect it."

There, it was out.

"Is it because of your health, Louis? I had hopes—it has been so much improved these past few years. Many of the Balfours have weak chests, but most of them outgrow it. Your grandfather Balfour did. Your mother, who was ill so much when you were a little lad, is now in splendid health, I'm thankful to say. So . . ."

"It's not my health," Louis said quietly. "I'm simply not cut out to be an engineer."

They trudged on in silence, without noticing the spring-green beauty around them. When he spoke at last, Mr. Stevenson's voice was calm.

"I'd not want it said I made you do what was wrong for you. Yet I feel it my duty to reason with you. You have not been a good student at the University. Still, I was young once myself. I well remember spending time in idle jests instead of serious study. In spite of that, I became a fair engineer."

"Fair!" Louis broke in. "You're brilliant! Everyone knows it."

"Now, Smout." A smile creased Thomas Stevenson's face when he used the old pet name. "I'm sure you'd do as well in spite of your truancy and pranks. Reports of your summer work with the men who were building lighthouses and breakwaters have all been favorable. I can't say the same for plans you've worked on in the office. But if you really apply yourself to studying mathematics—"

"The harder I try," Louis broke in, "the worse my mathematical problems turn out."

"That's pure nonsense. You would not have the friendship of a great professor of engineering like Fleeming Jenkin if you had not shown some skill—"

Louis interrupted again. "Father, I consider Fleeming one of my very best friends. But I assure you it is not engineering we discuss. He knows I'm no engineer—you can ask him. He thinks of me as a writer."

"We always come back to that," Thomas Stevenson said bitterly. "For a gentleman, writing is a fine hobby. But you cannot depend on it to earn a living. First learn a proession. Then you won't starve when you write."

"I never heard that Sir Walter Scott starved to death." Louis was bitter, too.

"Do you compare yourself—?" Mr. Stevenson stopped and went on more calmly. "That was unfair. You do show talent. Perhaps you are like Sir Walter in some ways. You both write well. You were both sickly children. And you are both members of the Spec."

For an instant, Louis' face brightened. "I *do* think the Spec. is the best thing in Edinburgh," he declared.

The Speculative Society was an old club. Many noted men in Scotland had been members. When the Spec. met in its lofty rooms at the University, the members would read a new essay. These essays and the hot debates which followed delighted Louis. He had felt greatly honored when he had been elected as a member. Suddenly now, it seemed to him that the Spec. could not really have wanted him.

"I'm afraid they only elected me because I am Robert Stevenson's grandson and your son," he told his father gloomily.

"I won't have you belittling yourself, Smout, just because we disagree," Mr. Steven-

son said more kindly. "And the Spec. woul
never choose a member because of his family
Now, getting back to Sir Walter Scott, let m
remind you that he was a lawyer before h
made a name as a writer. Law was wha
he studied at the University, and he had it t
fall back upon as a way of earning a living."

"There is a difference between being a law
student and one in engineering, Father,"
Louis said. "If I were studying law, I would
have more time for writing. Besides, I would
be studying subjects that might help me as
writer. That would be better than slaving a
mechanical drawing and mathematics which I
never will be able to master."

Mr. Stevenson pondered in silence for
long time. This was the end of his dream of
seeing his son take his place as a Lighthouse
Stevenson. Yet he was fair enough to admit that the law was an honorable profession.

"I cannot let you drop engineering simply
to write," he said at last slowly. "But if you
wish to study law instead, I shall help you."

Louis felt a lump in his throat. He knew
what those words had cost his father.

"Thank you, Father," he said. "I shall try to
make you proud of me yet. And I want you
to know that lighthouses—Grandfather's Bell

Rock and your Skerryvore and all the rest—do mean a great deal in my life. I'll never be happier than I've been when I went with you on inspection tours. It's just that I cannot build them myself. I can't even explain—"

"Don't try, then, Smout." Thomas Stevenson said gently. "We must go on and do the best we can."

Mrs. Stevenson and Cummie looked up quickly when the two of them came into Swanston Cottage together. They were an oddly assorted pair—Louis so tall and gangling, Thomas built as sturdily as one of his own lighthouses.

But Mrs. Stevenson sighed a little with relief. There was a new peace in both faces—a mixture of sadness and hope. It was good to have her husband and her son friends once more.

And Cummie saw something else in her Master Lou's eyes. The dreams were there again. She used to see them whenever he began telling a new story.

CHAPTER ELEVEN

The Savages Land on Cramond

THE wind blew close to gale force, whipping up steep waves in the Firth of Forth. It would make heavy going for even a sizable ship. Six boys on the beach at Cramond took turns peering through a telescope. They could hardly believe their eyes. Two canoes were struggling to reach the island. They looked frail as cockle-shells with foaming seas curling over them.

"Those men must be daft!" said George Lisle.

George was twelve years old, and the leader of the boys. Camping on the beach, they pretended to be wreckers. Now that it looked as if they would really have two wrecks on their hands, George felt uncomfortable.

"They're daft!" he repeated with a worried frown. "They'll never do it."

"I wouldn't be so sure," said Malcolm, who belonged to a seagoing family. "They handle those silly craft well. One of them might be Sir Walter Simpson. My big brother says he's been introducing canoeing in Scotland as a sport."

"Simpson?" asked another boy. "Isn't he the man who discovered chloroform? I thought he was dead. Or anyhow too old to be up to such tricks."

"That was his father, you oaf," Malcolm said scornfully. "This Sir Walter isn't old at all."

"And he never will be, if he keeps on picking weather like this," said George. "He'll make it this time, though. Look, they've got into the lee. Let's go down to meet them."

The boys scrambled over rocks and slippery seaweed. George sloshed into the waves and grasped the prow of the first canoe. Its boatman jumped ashore, a lanky, dark man who looked too frail to have come through such a battle with the sea. His sturdier companion, who was certainly not Sir Walter Simpson, was every bit as tired. Both young men were glad to have the help of six boys in pulling the canoe up above the high-water mark.

"We do thank you kindly." From the pocket of his velvet coat the dark man pulled a shiny shilling and handed it to George. "Tell me what other savages live upon this island?"

George was a bit nettled. "You must have forgotten your *Robinson Crusoe* or you would know it was the savages who came to the island in canoes. There were no savages here till you came."

Malcom gasped, and George realized that he had been quite impertinent. But the voyager didn't mind at all. They both laughed.

"You're fairly caught this time, Lou," Bob Stevenson told his cousin. "Wait till I warn Sir Walter that he is planning to take a canoe trip in France with a poor, ignorant heathen. And him expecting to travel with that famous author and lawyer, R. L. S."

Louis grinned at Bob's teasing, but he was secretly pleased. He was still very far from being famous, but he had made a start. *Cornhill Magazine* had published some of his stories which they allowed him to sign with his initials. This was a real honor. Most of their stories weren't signed at all.

Louis stretched out beside the boys' beach

re. He waved his legs in the air and let his
amp trousers steam. George watched him
vith surprise. He did not know how authors
behaved, for this was the first one he had met.
But the stiffest of all his uncles was a lawyer,
nd he could not imagine anyone more differ-
nt.

"Are you really a lawyer?" he asked.

It was Bob Stevenson who answered. "I'll
ave you know my distinguished cousin here
s a full-fledged lawyer. He can wear a wig and
own like any lawyer in Scotland whenever
e pleases. He can put up a brass plate with his
ame on it. For real dignity, you boys ought to
ave seen him the day he won his degree. He
drove through the town in the family ba-
ouche. He sat on top of the carriage with his
eet on the seat between his mother and father.
He waved his top hat and shouted the news to
verybody they passed. If that isn't dignified
egal behavior, I'd like to know what is."

George blinked. This was less than ever like
his uncle.

"What did your mother and father think
about such goings-on?" he asked Louis.

"They were so relieved that I had passed my
xams that they'd have overlooked anything
hat day," Louis said. "Now I have my degree,

I doubt if the courts of law will see much o
me. But it made my father happy, and that i
what counts."

Louis was very serious about this. Durin;
his student days, he and his father had no
been on good terms. Misunderstandings ha
made them both very miserable. They ha
differed over a number of things.

To avoid arguments, Louis had spent more
nd more time away from Heriot Row. He
sed to lean over the great bridge that joins
he Old Town and the New Town in Edin-
urgh. He watched the trains smoking under-
eath it and vanishing into a tunnel. He
onged to go with them and leave troubles be-
ind.

Because he was both lonely and rebellious Louis had made friends with fishwives and dockhands. He found the people of Edinburgh's steep slums more interesting than his parents' friends. Certainly it was good for him as a writer to learn how all kinds of people lived.

Even in inns like the *Green Elephant* where thieves and pickpockets gathered, he had met with nothing but kindness. Folk just called this strange young man "Velvet Coat" and left him alone to scribble away in his penny copybook. When he wasn't scribbling, Louis had joined in their jokes and their songs.

Thomas Stevenson had heard about this, of course. He had felt very unhappy because his only son seemed to be such an idler. With some idea of keeping Louis at home and out of trouble, he had allowed him very little pocket money. Five shillings a week was an absurd allowance for a University student, but Louis did not protest. He took the five shillings. Usually he spent it all the first day. Once he put the coins into the pocket of a ragged urchin he found asleep near the bridge. He liked to think of that boy's surprise when he woke up.

Another time Louis had found his own way

f making a little money. His mother and Aunt
ane were out driving one day with a prim
ady relative who was visiting Edinburgh.

"Will you look at that dreadful rag-and-
ones man!" the lady said suddenly. "He can't
ver have had a proper meal. And probably
never a bath either."

Mrs. Stevenson and Aunt Jane Balfour saw
he slouching, skinny figure carrying a sack
over the shoulder. Mrs. Stevenson tried to
muffle a scream. Aunt Jane turned a snort of
laughter into a cough. Oh dear, whatever
would their Louis be up to next? They did
not tell their starchy relative that they had
recognized the rag-and-bones man.

Louis could laugh about that now. But it
had been an unhappy time all the same. So unhappy that it had finally made him very ill.
Quarrels were forgotten then. All that mat-
tered to Mr. and Mrs. Stevenson was that Louis
must get well. When he was able to travel, they
had sent him first to England and then to the
south of France to regain his health.

Louis had not fallen back into the old
gloomy loneliness on his return to Edinburgh.
His parents were so happy to have him home
that there were no more disagreements. And,
best of all, Bob came back from studying art in

Paris. That had made all the differenc[

"I'm able to breathe again, Cummie,
Louis had told his old nurse, who still live
with the family at Heriot Row. "I'm done wit
the sullens for good. Now that Bob's here, I'v
got a friend to laugh with."

"Well, laughing is a good remedy for many problems," Cummie had admitted. "And I've no doubt there'll be mischief with the two of you together again."

So it had turned out. The two young men might almost be back in their old kingdoms of Nosingtonia and Encyclopedia. Their wild pranks and gay expeditions became the talk of Edinburgh. But the talk about "those crazy Stevensons" was friendly now instead of critical. People laughed at them and forgot that they had disapproved of Louis.

Bob was thinking about this as he warmed himself by the beach fire while the boys sat around in a respectful silence. He interrupted Louis' thoughts about his student days. "You and your father seem to be on the best of terms now," he said.

"We're the very best of friends again," Louis declared happily. He turned over to let the other side of his clothes dry at the fire. "And friends are—and always will be—my proudest possessions. There's you and Walter and Fleeming Jenkin and Sidney Colvin. And Leslie Stephen and Edmund Gosse and Andrew Lang—all men who've already made their names in literature. And our dear pirate, Henley."

"Och, now I know who *you* are!"

This exclamation from the youngest of the six boys quite startled the two cousins who were remembering the past.

"You're the man who came to the hospital to visit that poet, Mr. Henley, when they had to cut off his leg. My friends, Roden and Willie, were in the infirmary at the same time— and in the same room. They used to play at operations because they got so tired listening to grownups talk. But you and Mr. Henley weren't a bit like grownups, they told me. They said you talked about nothing but pirates. And that you knew *everything* about pirates!"

The six boys looked at Louis with added respect. A man who knew all about pirates was something special.

Louis rose to the occasion. He poked the fire up and told them blood-curdling tales of Henry Morgan and Blackbeard on the Spanish Main, and about the woman pirate, Ann Bonney, who was fiercer than the men she sailed with. He told them about the treasure Captain Kidd had buried on Gardiner's Island, not far from New York. "And very likely it's there yet if you want to make up an expedition to dig for it—"

"Don't forget Three-fingered Jack," Bob reminded Louis.

"As if I *could* forget." Louis' eyes shone as he recalled the day, so many years ago, when he and Bob had discovered the Kingdom of Skelt in a small stationery store.

Things had changed since then. Now Bob was a serious painter. Instead of coloring "penny plains," he would be leaving in a few days for the little town of Grez in France to paint important pictures. Louis was soon going to France, too, on the canoe trip with Sir Walter Simpson. That sounded like a holiday, but it wasn't altogether, because Louis was planning to write a book about it.

Yet, even though they were grown up, they didn't seem any older than the six boys who were begging for another pirate story.

"The sea is still running high, even if the wind has died," Malcolm pointed out. "The paddling will be so much easier in another hour, that you'll really save time in the end. You haven't told us about the LaFittes yet."

Time was forgotten. R. L. S., Teller of Tales, was proving how well he had learned his craft.

CHAPTER TWELVE

A Meeting in France

YOUNG LLOYD OSBOURNE breathed hard on the windowpane and drew a pattern with his finger. He pushed up the spectacles that kept slipping down his small nose. Behind him, his sixteen-year-old sister Belle was cleaning her paint brushes. From the river came the shouts of a party of young men in canoes. Lloyd wondered if one of them would be the "other Stevenson" he'd been hearing about.

"I do wish we had never come here to Grez," he muttered, scowling.

"Why, Lloyd!" Belle stared at her little brother in astonishment. "Grez is a perfectly lovely place. A river for boating. Pretty country to walk in. Lots of scenes for Mama and me to paint. I like Grez better than Paris. I even like it better than being home in California."

"The place is all right, I guess," Lloyd admitted. "It's all these artists with their jokes you can't understand and their horseplay that I don't think funny. Yesterday that Bob Stevenson upset the canoe he and Mama were in. And he knows Mama can't swim."

"But he fished her out of the river," Belle said. "Mama didn't mind. She thought it was fun. And *I* think Mr. Bob Stevenson is nice."

"Well, I don't. And there's going to be another one of them. I heard somebody saying that when those two Stevensons are together, everything is always in an uproar."

"The trouble with you," Belle said with sisterly bluntness, "is you're too young to understand. They're not dangerous as you make out. It's just the way grownups like us enjoy ourselves."

Lloyd snorted. Belle might be twice as old as he was, but she wasn't all that grown up. She hadn't played with him as she used to for a long time, though. Or even talked to him about sensible things like trains and ships and pirates, and how to get Mama to buy him a little printing press, and how to build a paddle-wheel steamer that could really run. This place would be better if he had some good company. The village children only laughed at his bad French and didn't understand a word he said.

"And anyway," Belle added, "Robert Louis Stevenson isn't a painter like his cousin Bob. He's a writer."

"What difference does that make?" Lloyd protested crossly. "I'm going to be a writer and print my own books, too, but I don't go pushing people out of canoes. And I bet he does."

His remark was greeted by a burst of laughter from the doorway where his mother and Bob Stevenson were coming in.

"Lloyd, dear, you're not still brooding about that, are you?" Fanny Osbourne smiled at her son. "I won't drown, believe me. I may not be able to swim, but I'm very good at floating."

"You are a magnificent floater," Bob said gallantly. "Probably the best floater the United States of America has ever produced. Your performance has given me a fine opinion of your great country. I have almost decided to tell Lou we should visit America. That is, if he hasn't already been shot!"

"Shot?" Belle asked.

"Some people," Bob explained, "could paddle simply and safely through the inland waters of Belgium and France. But not my cousin Louis. He has to be mistaken by one and all for a spy.

"I warned him that, if he refused to dress as a proper British gentleman should, he ought at least always to carry his passport. Again, not Louis. He clings to his outlandish clothes, including the most spy-looking cloak you ever saw. And he never knows where he has left any of his papers, including his passport. The only thing he never parts with is the notebook he uses to jot down scraps of poetry and ideas for stories."

"But he was with Sir Walter Simpson," Mrs. Osbourne protested. "Surely Sir Walter couldn't be mistaken for anything but a British nobleman. And I'm sure he would always carry his passport."

"Oh, Lou was safe so long as Walter was with him," Bob admitted. "But my cousin is a hard person to keep track of. And the French police did find him alone and without any papers except his notebook. So they promptly threw him into a dungeon.

"They only laughed at him when he said he was a Scotsman. No one from the British Isles could look as he did, they insisted. And no one from the British Isles could speak French so well. No, they said, he was a spy, and his notebook proved it. Obviously that was written in code."

"Your poor cousin!" said Mrs. Osbourne.

Bob laughed. "Don't waste your sympathy on him," he told her. "I'm sure Lou enjoyed every minute of it, dungeon and all. It was poor Walter who had the dull part when he finally discovered where Louis was.

"He had to prove who they were. And he had to convince the code expert who had spent hours over Lou's scribbles that he would never find any military secrets among all those words and scraps of phrases. The notebook held bits of poems, ideas for stories, and notes for his

[116]

book on that canoe trip. Lou intends calling that *An Inland Voyage,* but I think *In and Out of Gaol with a Canoe* would be a more apt title. I shall tell him so when he arrives this evening."

"He is coming then?"

"Yes, indeed. We're all waiting for him. There will be quite a party to greet him."

During the next hour more and more of Louis' friends came in until eighteen artists filled the big room with talk and laughter. It grew dark, and oil lamps were lighted. The babble of voices grew louder. Fanny Osbourne and Belle were in the midst of the gay crowd. But Lloyd went to sit by himself in a dark corner.

Lloyd was watching his mother when she turned and stared at the window. He looked, too, and saw a dark face peering into the room. It seemed to Lloyd to be staring at his mother with a surprised, happy look. As if it had suddenly found something it had been searching for.

The face vanished. A moment later the door flew open. Louis came in to be greeted with shouts of joy. Lloyd kept watching this dark man as he laughed and joked with the others. He seemed to bring more light into the room

Louis came in to be greeted by shouts of joy

with him, and a gaiety that even reached Lloyd in his corner. The terrible Stevenson didn't look so bad when you saw him in person.

"Hello, you must be Lloyd!" Louis had discovered the little boy. Unlike the other artists, he didn't just say hello and then go on. He pulled a chair around and straddled it, resting his chin on the back. Then he talked to Lloyd as if he were the most important person in the room.

Lloyd soon found himself telling Louis a great many things. About trout fishing in California. About his dream of owning a printing press. He talked as if Louis was one of his oldest friends. But Lloyd noticed that again and again Louis' eyes sought the spot where his mother was.

"Do you mind?" Louis said at last, pulling out his notebook. "I've just thought of something I might be able to use in my book. If I don't put it down now, I might forget it."

Lloyd watched the young man as he wrote with his notebook balanced on the back of the chair. He did not know what he was writing, but Lloyd had a strange feeling that it was somehow connected with his mother.

Louis wrote the lines that he would use at

[*119*]

the very end of his book, *The Inland Voyage:*

"You may paddle all day long; but it is when you come back at nightfall, and look in at the familiar room, that you find Love or Death awaiting you beside the stove; and the most beautiful adventures are not those we go to seek."

At the end of his voyage, Louis had found love. Indeed, he had fallen in love at first sight with Lloyd's mother Fanny.

CHAPTER THIRTEEN

Travels with a Donkey

Robert Louis Stevenson looked at Modestine. And Modestine looked at Robert Louis Stevenson.

"You do not have an excuse, not a single one," Louis told her. He walked around her and checked the girths and the baggage she carried. All was in order. Still Modestine would not move.

"You're simply stubborn!" Louis shouted in sudden exasperation. "If you don't move this instant, I'll beat you until you do."

He tugged at her bridle. Modestine braced her tiny hoofs.

Louis took out his pocket knife and went to the hedge. He selected a long, thin branch and cut it. He watched Modestine, and Modestine watched him as he trimmed off the leaves. He switched it a few times through

[*121*]

the air to test it. Then he began walking purposefully toward Modestine.

Modestine watched till he was only a few feet away. Then she ambled down the dusty trail as if that was what she had always intended to do.

Louis laughed. "You're the most opinionated, stubborn, exasperating beast I've ever met," he told the small, mouse-gray donkey.

Modestine brayed. It sounded as if she were saying, "You just wait."

Man and donkey trudged down the road together. Around them the mountains of the

Cévennes rose in the September sunlight. They had already spent several days in this wild, desolate country.

Louis had received plenty of warnings when he set out. There would be robbers, he was told. He would lose his way and starve. Or he would freeze to death in some high pass before rescuers could reach him. But no one had warned him about Modestine. So far he had had more trouble with the little donkey than with anything else. Still, she would give him plenty to write about. He thought *Travels with a Donkey* would make a good title for a book.

"Yes, Modestine, I shall expose your wayward ways. It will serve as a warning to others never to repeat my experiment."

In spite of having donkey trouble, Louis felt that this would be a happy trip. During the past two years he had become much better known as a writer. His *Inland Voyage* had been well received. He continued to write articles for *Cornhill Magazine*. The initials R. L. S. were beginning to have the fame he had dreamed about when he carved them in the tree at Swanston.

Louis had also published one of his best stories, *A Lodging for the Night*. And he had begun a new series of stories in a magazine that his poet friend Henley was now editing. The series was called *The New Arabian Nights*.

Bob had helped Louis work out some of the plots for the series. And a hilarious time the two of them had had, putting nonsense and adventure together so that they were not *quite* impossible and might happen any day right round the corner.

"Yes, Modestine, my fame is growing by leaps and bounds, even if I don't seem to earn much money."

It worried Louis that he still had to accept help from his father. His father was very glad to give the help. He pointed out that it was money Louis would one day inherit anyway, so he might as well have the use of it while he needed it. Thomas Stevenson was finally convinced that his son had been quite right in choosing writing as his career.

But Louis had a new problem now. It was Fanny Osbourne. He and Fanny had fallen in love, but marriage was a grave step to take. Fanny had insisted that Louis' parents would not approve of him marrying a woman older than himself with two children.

"Fanny feels every bit as young as I do," he

informed Modestine, "so what does it matter what year she was born? And no man could ask for more delightful stepchildren than Lloyd and Belle."

Modestine stopped to consider her master's words. She did not answer, however, but began to nibble the short grass. Louis stopped, too, and looked round. He had been so deep in thought that he had not noticed where his donkey was leading him.

They were no longer on a road, but on a path leading into the woods. When he tried to retrace his steps, Louis found other paths crisscrossing, and he could not decide which was the right one. He realized that Modestine had succeeded in losing their way.

Worse still, it was getting toward nightfall, and the black clouds of a thunderhead were building up in the sky.

"How could you do this to me, Modestine?" Louis demanded. "Do you know what my doctor said when I told him about this trip? 'I hope you won't be so foolish as to camp out in wet weather.' Those were his very words. But you don't worry about my health, do you? To tell you the truth, I don't worry about my health either. So we'll strike camp right here before the storm reaches us. If my sleeping bag is as good as I hope, you'll be the one to get soaked."

Modestine did get soaked. So did Louis, for the storm came up fast. However, it was soon past. Louis managed to find enough dry wood to start a fire and soon steamed gratefully beside it.

"Quite like a pioneer," he told Modestine on the other side of the blaze. "Or a prospector with his faithful burro. Tell me, Modestine, if I should follow Fanny to California, would you come along and be my faithful burro? No, you prefer to stay in France? Well, I wish Fanny had stayed here instead of deciding she ought to take her children back to their own country. California is so far away."

Now more or less dry, Louis began preparing his supper. Modestine was suddenly all sweetness. She was every bit as gentle as her last master had claimed when he had sold her to Louis.

"You don't fool me with your pretty airs and graces, so there will be nothing extra for you tonight," Louis told her. "Only an idiot would be fooled by you. And wasn't I the idiot the day I bought you?"

Louis laughed, remembering how her owner had said that Modestine was the gentlest donkey alive—so gentle that any child could ride her. To prove his point, the man had chosen a child from the crowd and set her on Modestine's back. Modestine promptly bucked the child off. Another child was called. That one went over Modestine's head. A third slid off when Modestine sat down.

After that, strangely, the crowd that had gathered to watch the foreigner buy a donkey had simply melted away. Not a child was left to continue the experiment.

"And yet I bought you."

Louis rubbed Modestine's nose. Modestine lowered her long eyelashes and nuzzled Louis —or his pocket. Modestine loved brown bread, and Louis was soon giving her the piece he had cut for himself.

CHAPTER FOURTEEN
Silverado Squatters

ALTHOUGH it was only a little past nine o'clock, Silverado was already sweltering under the California sun. Once it had been a busy camp. But when the silver mine that gave it its name failed, it quickly fell into ruins. It could hardly even be called a ghost town. Virtually the only building still standing had once been a combination office, cookhouse, and bunkhouse.

But the place was not quite deserted. Recently a couple had moved there who called themselves King and Queen of Silverado. With them was their young Crown Prince Lloyd.

It was the Crown Prince who now trotted up a precarious board walk to the ramshackle

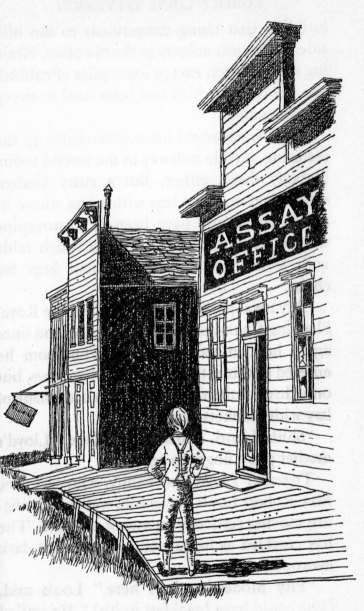

*The Crown Prince now trotted up a
precarious board walk*

building that clung dangerously to the hill side. There was nobody in the old office. Nothing there, either, except some piles of rubbish and the broom which had been used to sweep them together.

The Prince edged his way carefully up the teetering outside stairway to the second room. Nobody there, either. But a rusty kitchen stove stood on three legs with a box where its fourth leg should have been. The stovepipe was brand new, and there was a rough table with some dishes on it and nail kegs for chairs.

"My royal parents must be still in the Royal Sleeping Chamber," said the Prince, and once again he climbed the stairs. The room he entered now had thirty bunks in two rows, but only three of them were in use as beds made of hay with blankets over them.

"Shhh, Lloyd, Louis is still asleep." Lloyd's mother put a finger to her lips.

Together Lloyd and Fanny, who was now Mrs. Robert Louis Stevenson, watched the figure moving restlessly on one of the beds. The hay crackled as he turned over, and his dark eyes opened.

"Pity Modestine isn't here," Louis said. "She could have breakfast in bed." He smiled at his wife and stepson. "I had a nightmare, so I'm glad to wake up. I almost expected to find myself back in Heriot Row with Cummie there to tell me a story."

"I wish your Cummie had been here yesterday," his wife said. "Perhaps she could have stopped you from getting too tired. You're not well enough to walk all day in the hot sun."

"Why, Fanny, I assure you I'm as healthy as can be." Louis grinned when he realized that he must sound very much as he did when he was little. "As a matter of fact, it was *your* illness that gave me the nightmare. Your illness that brought me to California."

Louis had been in Scotland when he received a letter saying that Fanny was ill and that she missed him terribly. He had decided at once that he must go to her. All his friends had been so shocked at his idea of going far away to California that he hadn't dared to tell his parents. He had written them after he had embarked on the steamship *Devonia,* bound for New York.

The Atlantic voyage had been a stormy one, but Louis was still enough of a Lighthouse Stevenson not to get seasick. The steerage passengers were emigrants from a good many countries. Louis made friends with them all.

He took care of them when they were sick. He
entertained their children. When the weather
improved, he sang their native songs with
them and danced their native dances to tunes
from an accordion.

He had enjoyed the journey across the
ocean. But his two weeks in an emigrant train
crossing the United States were far more trying. The cars were poorly lighted and hardly
aired at all. Wooden benches made uncomfortable sitting for bony Louis. He found it almost impossible to sleep on them. Passengers
bought food at way stations from farm women,
and cooked it on the stove in the end of the
car.

Cooped up together, the travelers grew
short-tempered. Sometimes the quarreling
and the crying children and the smells drove
Louis to desperation. Then he would climb up
to sit on the top of the car. It was a dangerous
perch from which to view endless miles of
prairie, but it did have air. It was smoky air,
and Louis always returned cinder-black.

Having very little money, Louis had not
been able to eat properly on his journey. He
was quite ill by the time he reached California.
Since he did not want Fanny to see him in
that condition, he decided to camp out for a

few days to recover. For two nights he lay out under the trees near Monterey in a kind of stupor. He would have died there had it not been for two frontiersmen in charge of a goat ranch. They carried him to their cabin and nursed him until he was able to care for himself again.

Louis had liked Monterey, which was still a very Mexican town. Men rode through the streets in dramatic vaquero style. In the evenings they serenaded their señoritas.

Before going on to San Francisco, Louis had decided he would like to see the Point Pinos Lighthouse. The keeper was a silent man who did not welcome visitors. But this visitor could have stayed forever when the keeper learned that he was a member of the family of Lighthouse Stevensons. It made Louis feel very much at home to hear this man thousands of miles from Edinburgh talking about the work of Thomas Stevenson.

Fanny had recovered from her illness by the time Louis had arrived in San Francisco.

"It's strange how life works out," Louis told his wife, raising himself on his elbow in his bunk. "I came to America to nurse you, and it was you who had to nurse me. Now, if the Queen and the Crown Prince of Silverado will vacate the Royal Bedchamber, the King wil get up for breakfast. Eggs and bacon, please And is there a bit of marmalade for the roya piece of toast?" Louis looked at his stepson "What have you been up to, Lloyd? You're fairly bursting with news."

"I've been discovering things," Lloyd ad mitted. "But you'll have to come and see then for yourself. I'd have some toast with you first if you asked me."

While Louis dressed, he thought how lucky they had been to find Silverado. He had worked very hard in San Francisco, sending his writ ings to publishers in England and then waiting endlessly to be paid for them. At his boarding house, he had nursed his landlady's little daughter through a dangerous illness. Then he had become dangerously ill himself. So ill that he wrote Sidney Colvin that his new address was Death's Door. He had even scrib bled a sketch of his tomb and made up a poem for his epitaph. It began:

> "*Under a wide and starry sky*
> *Dig the grave and let me lie. . . .*"

That was when Fanny Osbourne had be gun to take care of him. Louis was now glad to wait a few years before using the epitaph. His arents had forgiven him for marrying Fanny. And his father had sent money enough to last them until he could begin earning some again.

"Our fortune smiles as bright as this New World sun," Louis said when he sat down to breakfast. "We are monarchs of all we survey. All we need is Belle and that young artist she is going to marry, and we could start a kingdom in earnest. And when we buy Lloyd his printing press, he can publish our doings in the Court Chronicle."

"How did you know I want a printing press?" Lloyd asked.

Louis and Fanny laughed loudly. Lloyd did not realize it, but very few days passed without him mentioning his dream.

"The very first time I met you—remember it?—you talked about a printing press," Louis told him. "In the four years since then, I've heard considerably more about it. Don't give up hope—it's getting closer. But now, let's go and see what you've discovered."

Lloyd had a number of interesting things to point out to Louis, for he had been very busy at his exploring. He had found the old entrance to the mine—a dank tunnel that went back into the hillside.

"Don't you go in there—at any rate not

without me—*ever*," Louis told his stepson
"The timbers that hold up that earthen roo
are rotted and all chewed by insects."

"There's a very funny noise there," Lloyd
said. "That was my real discovery. I've been
waiting for it. It was awfully clear before. Now
—listen!"

They both heard it.

"Now who would be shaking dry peas in a
paper sack up here?" Louis asked. "Or is tha
what it really sounds like? Maybe more like a
boy's top spinning on a wooden sidewalk. Bu
that isn't likely either."

Again and again they heard the noise, bu
they could not discover what caused it. The
mystery was not solved that day or the next.

It was not solved, in fact, until shortly before
they left Silverado to go back to Scotland.

That day Lloyd and Lou met a grizzled old
prospector who had been searching for silver
Louis stopped to admire the man's burro. She
reminded him of Modestine.

Suddenly both he and Lloyd heard the same
noise as had come from the tunnel. This time
the noise was very clear and quite loud.

Louis had no time to look for its source be
fore the prospector drew his revolver and fired
four shots. Louis was puzzled. He had been

They met a grizzled old prospector

told that these old prospectors got a bit queer in the head. But he didn't think just patting the man's burro should irritate him that much. Certainly, the shots had seemed to be aimed at Louis himself. Or at least at his feet. What was wrong?

The prospector gave him the answer. He stepped past Louis and picked up the rattlesnake he had just killed.

"Son," he said, "when you hear those rattles you ought to jump. This critter was aimin' to strike, and you ain't even wearin' boots. If he'd got his fangs into you, it would 'a' plumb spoiled my day. It's too dang hot for grave diggin'."

In a flash Louis remembered the epitaph he had written for himself. At Silverado he realized the sky was particularly "wide and starry." He had been lucky to escape the rattlesnake. It was too beautiful a day to die!

CHAPTER FIFTEEN

Treasure Island

IT WAS in August, 1880, that Louis took Fanny and Lloyd home to Scotland. He was sure that his father and mother would like Fanny, and he was not disappointed. Thomas Stevenson became especially fond of his daughter-in-law, who called him Uncle Tom.

"Precisely the right wife for you, Smout," he told his son. He used that pet name still whenever he was particularly happy. "You'll be wise if you never publish anything Fanny does not think worth while. I'm proud to have her in our family. And that goes for young Lloyd—I like the lad."

His father's approval meant a great deal to Louis. So did the warm welcome they had from Bob and all his other friends. Sir Walter Simpson called at Heriot Row, bringing a very wriggly gift. It was a black Skye terrier puppy to fill Coolin's place. Fanny and Louis both fell in love with the little dog at first sight.

"We'll name him after you," Louis told Sir Walter. He leaned down and lightly tapped the squirming puppy with a pencil. "I dub thee Sir Walter—you imp!" The puppy had rolled over to grab the pencil in needle-sharp teeth.

Sir Walter was too grand a title for such a small dog. At least for everyday use. The name was changed to Walt, to Wattie, then to Woggs. Finally, no one quite knew how, it became Bogue, and Bogue it stayed.

Louis had been far from well since his days in California. His Uncle George Balfour, famous doctor, told Louis it was impossible for him to spend the winter in Edinburgh. He advised the climate of the high Alps.

At Davos in Switzerland, Louis found the climate helpful, but he did not enjoy the mountains or being in a colony of sick people.

"The mountains are like a trap about me," he complained to Fanny. "You cannot foot it up a hillside to behold the sea as you can at home. You live in holes and corners and can change only one for the other."

Tobogganing was the only thing Louis enjoyed at Davos. And that he liked alone and on a starry night. Then he felt as if he were flying through glimmering space, and he did not have to see the mountains looming everwhere. The rest of the time he was so homesick that he began writing poetry about his native land:

"Bells upon the city are ringing in the night,
  High above the gardens are the houses full of light.
  On the heathy Pentlands is the curlew flying free,
  And the broom is blowing bonny in the north
    countrie."

He was very glad when he could return to a cottage at Braemar in Scotland, where his mother and father could be with them often, and where Cummie came for a long visit. The house in Braemar never had had a name, but was known throughout the district simply as "the late Miss MacGregor's cottage." Even Louis had to admit it was not the most cheerful place in the world. It was always damp when it rained. And it rained a great deal.

Lloyd decided Scotland was the wettest place in the whole world. "Are you sure it was Moses you wrote about when you won your Uncle David's prize?" he asked his stepfather. "It ought to have been Noah and the Flood."

It was not only the rain that was making Lloyd unhappy. Just before they left Silverado he had finally got his printing press. He'd barely learned how to use it properly at Davos, and by accident, it had been left there. Louis had promised him that next winter they would really print a newspaper. They were going to call it *The Yallobally Record*. But winter seemed to Lloyd a long way off.

To make matters worse, he had to listen to his stepfather's lectures.

Louis had learned the University of Edinburgh would soon need a professor of law. He decided he ought to try for the job so he could support his new family properly without his father's help. So he prepared lectures and tried them out on poor Lloyd.

Lloyd found law the dreariest subject he could imagine. Louis thought it pretty dull, too, but he wasn't admitting it yet. Lloyd sighed after listening to an hour-long lecture.

"I do wish you would write something interesting instead of all this stuff," he had muttered one day.

Louis had only laughed. But Lloyd felt badly whenever he remembered what he had said. He had not meant to be so rude. And he had enjoyed *Travels with a Donkey* and *An Inland Voyage*. He liked *The Amateur Emigrant* and *The Silverado Squatters* when Louis wrote them. But most of Louis' work was

meant for grownups. It wasn't nearly so exciting as Louis was himself when they played together—especially war games when they were
Colonel Stevenson and General Osbourne.

One day Lloyd was drawing a map. He
wasn't much interested in it, but what else
was there to do on a rainy afternoon? His
mother and old Mr. Stevenson were reading.
Bogue was asleep. In spite of Lloyd's pokes in
his fat sides, he insisted on staying asleep.

"Well, that saves my having to take him for
a walk," Louis said.

"You are certainly not to go out until it
stops raining," Fanny told her husband.

"*If* it ever stops raining," Lloyd muttered.

"Lloyd, sometimes I think you don't ap-
preciate the weather of my native land," Louis
said. "As for me, I say this is better than the
everlasting snow at Davos. I love it."

"You may love it, but it doesn't love you,"
Fanny said. "The Alps are better for you."

"I know. I know. But they are so far from
the sea. What I really want is what Lloyd is
drawing, a nice warm island."

"An island?" Thomas Stevenson promptly
got up from his chair to see.

"That fetches you, doesn't it, Father?" Louis
said with a grin.

ROBERT LOUIS STEVENSON

"Well, it *is* an island," Lloyd said, puzzled.
"But how did you know it was a warm one?"
Louis laughed. "By the shape of it, my lad.

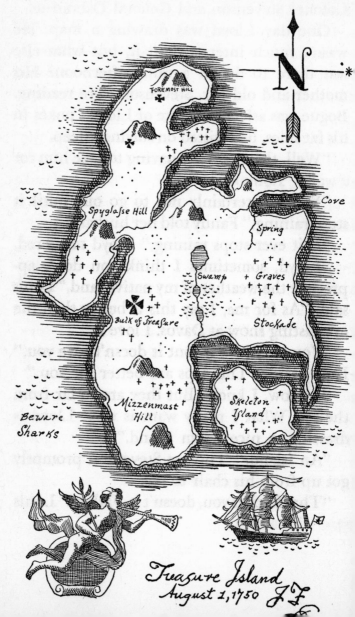

Treasure Island
August 1, 1750   J F

It seems to me you don't know very much about your own place. What is this, for example?" He picked up the pencil and neatly put in an X.

Lloyd didn't know.

"That is where the treasure is buried," whispered Thomas Stevenson. "An X always meant that, from the time Smout drew his first map."

Louis kept the pencil and used it. On the west coast he lettered *Spyglasse Hill*. "That's where our marooned sailor watches for a sail. Here's *Haulbowline Head,* and this smaller island in this cove is *Skeleton Island.*"

"But who put the treasure there?" Lloyd demanded. "And does your marooned sailor know it's there?"

"Now who *did* put the treasure there?" Louis mused. "I must ask my friend Henley —he'd be sure to know. Maybe he was the pirate who put it there himself. Henley's always looked more like a pirate than a poet, with his wild yellow hair and bushy beard. Why, with that wooden leg he has and a gold ring in his ear and a red kerchief round his head, he'd make an ideal pirate."

"You can't say that about a poet, can you?" Lloyd was a bit shocked.

"The Old Sea Dog at the Admiral Benbow"

"Well, as a pirate he would have another name, of course. How about Bill Silverado? Silverado—or something like that—wouldn't make a bad name for a pirate. I wonder if that island has any rattlesnakes. I don't see why not. But now who would have the map? That will take a bit of thinking out . . ." Louis started to the door with the map in his hand.

"Hey, that's mine!" Lloyd protested, wondering what Louis could possibly want with it.

He got his answer next morning when his mother told him Louis wanted to see him. Lloyd found him propped up against his pillows with a sheaf of papers in his hands.

"What—" Lloyd began.

"Just sit down and keep still," Louis said.

Lloyd sat down, but his heart sank right through the floor. Was he going to have to listen to *another* of those long lectures about Law? He didn't think he could bear it. Then he caught a glimpse of the map they had made yesterday, and his eyes grew round.

"Chapter I.," Louis read. "The Old Sea Dog at the Admiral Benbow. . . ."

Lloyd's wish for an exciting story had been answered. A story about pirates and a rascally sea cook. This was the beginning of *Treasure Island*.

CHAPTER SIXTEEN
R. L. S. Is Famous

NEVER again did Lloyd complain that his stepfather wrote dull books. The whole family lived the story of *Treasure Island* as it progressed from day to day. Thomas Stevenson even named Flint's old ship. He worked out the contents of Billy Bones' sea chest. He had a very fine map of the island drawn in his own office and properly engraved.

"I've a neat fist with a pen," Thomas told his son. "I'll *forge* those different handwritings you need for your story." And he did it.

Lloyd felt strongly that it was *his* book. He was delighted when the story was published as a serial in *Young Folks Magazine*. Its title then was *The Sea Cook,* and the author's name was given as George North. But two years later the story became a real book, and that was Lloyd's real triumph. For under the title, *Treasure Island,* was the dedication:

> To Lloyd Osbourne
> An American Gentleman
> In accordance with whose classic taste
> The following narrative has been designed.
> It is now, in return for numerous delightful hours
> And with the kindest wishes, dedicated
> by his affectionate friend
> THE AUTHOR

That made Lloyd just about the best known schoolboy in the British Isles when he was sent to school in England.

Louis had had a great many essays in magazines. But this was his first published book, so he was as excited as Lloyd. Moreover, the publishers had paid him a hundred pounds before the book was put on sale. This advance was the most money he had ever made. It seemed a real fortune when he wrote his mother and father:

"There has been offered for *Treasure Island*—how much do you suppose? It would be an excellent jest to keep the answer till my next letter, and for two cents I would do it . . . No—well—a hundred pounds, all alive—O! A hundred jingling, tingling, golden-minted quid . . ."

The book sprang into instant popularity. It was not only boys who enjoyed it. Sober and

noted men became boys once again as they sa
up reading into the small hours of the night
Mr. Gladstone, the Prime Minister, saw it at a
friend's house and did not rest until he had a
copy of his own. It was translated into many
different languages. It even appeared serially
in Greek and Spanish newspapers.

All over the world men and boys—and often
girls as well—were chanting one song:

> *"Fifteen men on the Dead Man's Chest—*
> *Yo-ho-ho and a bottle of rum!*
> *Drink and the devil had done for the rest—*
> *Yo-ho-ho and a bottle of rum!"*

Kidnapped was the book that followed
Treasure Island. David Balfour, the hero, was
one of Louis' ancestors. Alan Breck had actu
ally lived. The Alison in the story who ferried
Alan and David across the water was one of
Cummie's people. The Island of Earrid, where
David was shipwrecked, was the spot where
Louis had worked on his father's Dhu
Heartach Lighthouse.

So it went with most of the many books that
followed these stories. There was a great deal
of fact in them as well as imagination. And
most of the settings were places Robert Louis
Stevenson loved most dearly.

But they were also places he could only see

ow in his mind's eye. It was impossible for
im to live in Scotland any longer. The doc-
ors were all agreed on that.

At first the Stevensons went back to Davos,
where Louis and Lloyd finally published their
allobally Record until Lloyd had to go away
o school. But Louis never did like Davos.
When it turned out that the place was bad for
anny's health he refused to stay there. So he
nd Fanny spent many months in the south
f France.

They were happiest in their lovely house
n Hyères. But it was there that Louis had his
most severe illness. He came very close to
lying. Bob came to Hyères to help Fanny
urse him, but for weeks it looked hopeless.

Finally the doctor told Fanny one day,
Madame, if you can keep that man alive until
e is forty years old, you might have him till
e's ninety. But I tell you frankly, the chances
re slim."

In spite of the doctor's prediction Louis
lowly gained strength. Fanny knew that he
was lonely for his parents, so she wrote Thomas
Stevenson that she thought some place on the
outh coast of England would suit him as well
s France. Then Mr. and Mrs. Stevenson could
ive with them most of the year.

Mr. Stevenson's reply was immediate. He bought a fine house at Bournemouth right on the coast and presented it to his daughter-in-law.

Louis' parents were already there and had the house all ready when Fanny and Bob brought Louis from France. Louis loved every room of it. He loved the fine view of the sea and the salt breeze. Bogue immediately started digging up the garden. He set out to keep every other dog in Bournemouth in his proper place. Especially big dogs, for in his whole short life it never once occurred to Bogue that he was a *little* dog.

When the first inspection of the house was over, Thomas Stevenson looked at his son for his verdict.

"We'll call it *Skerryvore* for your first light-house, Father."

The old man smiled, but there was a tear in his eye. "Smout," he said, "you're still a Lighthouse Stevenson at heart."

"That I am, Father," Louis agreed cheerfully. "And shall be all my life long."

Louis' health was never worse than during the three years he spent at Bournemouth. He was seldom able to go beyond his garden gate.

"I live like a weevil in a biscuit," he said, but he laughed. He was the most cheerful of invalids. Friends thronged to Skerryvore. The rooms rang with laughter.

Louis never worked harder or accomplished

more than he did there. He worked in bed. He worked out of bed. He turned out poems and plays and short stories and novels. He finished putting together verses which he had begun long before. There were enough of them to make a book. At first he called it *Penny Whistles*. Then he changed the title to *A Child's Garden of Verses*.

The child was himself. All his days at Colinton and Heriot Row were in those pages. Aunt Jane was there, and his cousins, Willie and Henrietta. When the book was ready for the printers, Louis wrote the dedication to Cummie:

> *To Alison Cunningham*
> *From her Boy*
> *For the long nights you lay awake*
> *And watched for my unworthy sake;*
> *For your most comfortable hand*
> *That led me through the uneven land;*
> *For all the story books you read;*
> *For all the pains you comforted:*
>
> *. . . . .*
>
> *From the sick child, now well and old,*
> *Take, Nurse, the little book you hold."*

Cummie may have cried a little when she first held that book. Louis was certainly not well. He would never be old. But he was still her Boy. It wasn't long after the book was published that people began going to see Cummie in her own little cottage to ask her questions about him.

R. L. S. was now a famous man. People wanted to know all about him when he was a little lad. Cummie was very proud of her Boy. She was also the same sensible Cummie she had always been.

"He was like any other bairn," she would tell folks. "Whiles very naughty."

Another book came out of Skerryvore in Bournemouth that made Louis even more famous. It began with a nightmare. In the small hours after midnight, Fanny found Louis tossing and moaning in his sleep. She woke him to stop the nightmare. But Louis was angry.

"Now why did you wake me?" he protested. "I was dreaming a fine bogey tale."

The dream was so vivid that Louis wrote the first draft of the story in three days. It was called *The Strange Case of Dr. Jekyll and Mr. Hyde*. It was about a man who was really two men. He had two personalities, one of them good and the other bad. When it was finished, Louis showed it to his wife.

Fanny Stevenson was an honest woman. She did not like the story as it stood, and she said so. It was only a bogey tale now, she said. It should be more than that. It should have an "underneath" meaning.

Later she was downstairs when she heard Louis' bell ringing. She found him lying back against his pillows, coughing. He pointed a long, skinny finger at the fireplace where a spiral of smoke rose from a charred mass of paper.

Fanny rushed to pull it out and try to save at least some of it. But Louis stopped her. He had come to the conclusion that she was perfectly right. The story wasn't good enough now. His father had told him he must always take his wife's advice in such matters. He was doing so. He rewrote the whole thing in another three days.

This time it did have an "underneath" meaning. It created a sensation when it was published. Sermons were preached about it. Everybody read it. It sold many thousands of copies in England. It was even more popular in America.

Thomas Stevenson died a year after *Dr. Jekyll and Mr. Hyde* was published. It was clear that Louis' health was never going to improve in the English climate. Now there was no reason for them to stay in Bournemouth, since old Mrs. Stevenson was willing to travel wherever Louis and his family went. Louis thought Fanny and her son ought to see their American relations.

The Royal Albert Docks were crowded with friends to see him off when he sailed with his family on the S.S. *Ludgate Hill*. Fanny had left Louis to choose their ship and get the tickets. She should have known better. Not until they were aboard did she learn that her husband had booked their passage in a ship carrying a very odd cargo. The *Ludgate Hill's* freight consisted of stallions, apes, and matches.

It was a rough crossing, and poor Fanny was very seasick. But Louis had a grand time. One of the baboons decided Robert Louis Stevenson was the most wonderful human being it had ever met. It rode everywhere about the ship on his shoulder, hugging him affectionately. When Louis brought the baboon to their cabin to cheer Fanny, she did not want to see it.

Lloyd had almost as much fun as Louis on that trip. *Almost*. For Louis didn't mind *anything*—even taking care of seasick monkeys and stallions. When they finally reached New York harbor, Lloyd realized what a very famous man his stepfather was.

Two little pilot boats were sent out to bring in the S.S. *Ludgate Hill*. Their pilots were as different as any two men could be. The pleasant one had been nicknamed *Jekyll*. And everybody called the surly fellow *Hyde*.

CHAPTER SEVENTEEN
The Island Kingdom

"OH, CAPTAIN dear, and where has your mainmast gone?" sang the passengers aboard the trading schooner *Janet Nicholl*. She was a long, rakish craft, painted black. She rolled dreadfully. Throughout all the islands of the South Seas she was known as the *Jumping Jenny*.

The captain looked at his passengers. They were Louis and Fanny; Lloyd and Belle and Belle's little son Austin; and Mrs. Thomas Stevenson, whose prim Edinburgh life had been changed for one of adventure in her old age.

The mainmast *was* gone, lost in a storm. But that was not the sort of thing passengers would sing to a quick-tempered captain unless they were his very good friends. The captain just grinned. He had never known people he liked better.

Losing the mainmast was not the only calamity that had overtaken the *Jumping Jenny* on this voyage. One rough day's journey on their way, some fireworks which had been stored in the main cabin had blown up.

"Think nothing of it," Fanny had told the captain. "That is the sort of thing that always happens wherever Louis is."

The *Jumping Jenny* was not the first sail-

ing ship they had chartered to roam among the islands of the South Seas. These were islands that Louis had promised himself long ago he would visit. He had made that promise on the day Aunt Jane had showed him the wing of an albatross at Colinton Manse.

Louis had also told Aunt Jane he was sure he could make friends with cannibals, if he was careful always to arrive after dinner. But he ran no risk of being eaten for dinner when he first visited a cannibal isle. By that time the natives had been converted by mission-

aries. They no longer ate people, but they managed a fine feast of roast pig and pineapples for all the Stevensons.

Fanny and Louis both liked to tease old Mrs. Stevenson about this. Louis often said, "To think that my own mother has feasted with a native chieftain who has killed thousands of people and eaten hundreds!"

"Don't exaggerate," Mrs. Thomas Stevenson always replied tartly. "You know perfectly well he never ate but *eleven* poor souls."

It was aboard the yacht *Casco* that they had visited those cannibal isles. And it had come about because of Louis' health.

He had thoroughly enjoyed being treated as a famous man in New York, but it had exhausted him. The climate was not good for him. So he had been sent by one of his doctors to Saranac in the northern part of New York State. But he had not liked the Adirondack Mountains very much better than he had liked the Alps. The trouble was, you couldn't catch sight nor smell of the sea in those places. That was when he had had the idea of cruising the whole Pacific Ocean. He had sent Fanny ahead to California to see about hiring a boat with a captain and crew to take them where he wanted to go.

It was on June 15th, 1888, that the *Casco* put out through San Francisco's Golden Gate with the Stevensons aboard. She set her course for Honolulu and the Sandwich Islands. Before the trip on the *Casco* was ended, the Stevensons had made friends with cannibal chiefs and tall warriors and tattooed Polynesian queens, and with Kalakua, the King of Honolulu, who became Louis' special friend. They had all lived for two months in the King's house. Then they had gone on to the New Hebrides. Louis thrived in the warmth of the southern seas. He was in splendid health and tearing spirits.

The next craft on which they went a-voyaging was the *Equator,* a trading schooner that always smelled of her cargo of copra. She had a way of staggering and then swooping like a barnswallow in a storm. In her they met rain, calms, squalls. When it rained she was a *very* wet ship. And still Louis had not caught even one cold as they cruised through the Marshall Islands and the Gilberts. He and Lloyd had begun planning the first full-length book they were going to write together. It was called *The Wrecker,* and the story had been in Louis' mind from his first trip with his father aboard the old *Pharos.*

The *Equator* had carried them to the island of Samoa, where they had fallen in love with the place and the people.

Louis had decided he would like to settle in Samoa. But first he wished to go home to England to see all his friends and wind up his affairs. So off they sailed for Sydney, Australia, where they hoped to board another boat for England. In Sydney Louis promptly became very ill. Australian doctors all said he must never quit the tropical climate, and warned him that if he returned to Europe, even for the summer, he would surely die.

It was then that they had met the captain of the *Jumping Jenny,* and now they were on their way back to Samoa aboard the long, black schooner. They arrived on the island in November, 1890.

Fanny and Louis lived in a rough shack while their house was being built. They planned to call the house Vailima, which means Five Rivers.

The house was hardly started when Fanny began their garden. She could make things grow anywhere. Here, where soil and climate were so good, she soon had such a tropical garden as could hardly be imagined anywhere else.

Louis cut paths through heavy bush. A stinging plant blistered his skin. He was nearly hanged on a tough liana vine. It didn't matter. He was having a wonderful time.

Vailima was finished at last. The furniture which had been brought from England was installed, and it went very well with the mats woven by the natives of the island. A marble bust of old Grandfather Robert Stevenson looked serenely across the great hall at some grinning heathen idols.

This was truly the island kingdom of Louis' old dreams. Many Samoans came to help with the housework, to take care of the cows and the pigs, and to work in the fields. They looked upon Louis as their chief. He acted as their chief, too, settling disputes, looking after their health. He led them at feasts and at prayers. Like a real Scottish chief, he designed a tartan for the Vailima men to wear on ceremonial occasions.

These Samoan workers called Louis' wife Aolele, which means Flying Cloud, because she was forever busy about the house and estate. Very lovingly, they bestowed upon Louis the name, Tusitala, which means Teller of Tales.

Louis had been very much surprised when he arrived in Samoa to find that the natives there already had heard one of his stories. A missionary had translated *The Bottle Imp* into the Samoan language.

And to the Samoans, this tale of a genie in a bottle, able to grant wishes, seemed wholly true. The first native visitors to Vailima had carefully looked around for the bottle itself. They were sure that only a genie could have given such a beautiful home and such a large estate.

In one wing of his house, Louis had his own room, which was a workroom and bedroom combined. There he wrote his stories or dictated them to Belle, who carefully wrote down everything he said. When the day's writing was finished, Louis walked or rode with Lloyd or with Austin and a little Samoan boy named Pola. Louis had given Pola a pony exactly the color of his own lovely brown skin.

Pola was always bubbling over with fun. He chattered and sang all day long. He made up little verses and was deliriously happy when he was allowed to turn the handle of a hand organ. Louis gave him a box of tin soldiers, and they played together. When Pola lined up his troops he would talk to himself in Samoan: "These are brave brown men. They fight for Mataafa. Boom! Boom!"

Mataafa was a native king and Louis' very good friend. And it was because of Mataafa that Louis became involved in a brief, but real war.

The government of Samoa was very complicated at that time. The island was governed by three nations in turn, Britain, Germany, and the United States. When a German became president, the natives rebelled because he deposed their King Mataafa in favor of a monarch named Malietoa who was always willing to do exactly as he was told.

Louis did his best to keep the peace and get fair treatment for all. It was useless. The German president tried to force him to leave Samoa and wrote the British government that he was a troublemaker. The government of Great Britain took no notice. But in any case, before their reply could have been received, the war had broken out.

The Vailima woods became full of scouting parties. One day when Belle was taking dictation from Louis, she saw a warlike procession cross the lawn.

"Louis, have we a pistol or gun in the house that will *shoot?*" Belle asked.

"No," said Louis calmly, "but we have friends on both sides." He went on with his book.

After dinner, a messenger arrived with a note. The shooting had started. The wounded were arriving at the Mission House. Louis, Fanny, and Lloyd saddled their horses and rode through the dark night to help care for the men who had been hurt.

Louis' personal sympathies were with his friend, Mataafa. He felt real grief when Mataafa was defeated and promptly banished to another island. And he was furious when he was told that the chiefs who had fought for Mataafa were being held in the prison at Apia after they had been flogged through the streets.

Louis went down at once to the dirty jail, laden with food for the starving prisoners. He paid a doctor to attend to their wounds. He himself helped to clean up the filthy prison. That so shamed the men in charge of the jail that conditions began to improve rapidly.

When their year of imprisonment was over, eight of the chiefs went to Vailima to express their gratitude to Robert Louis Stevenson. They expressed it in more than words. A road was badly needed through dense jungle to connect Vailima with the main highway which ran across the island. The Samoans hated to work with their hands and felt that road making was degrading to warriors. Yet the chiefs cut this one for Louis even before they went home to their own people. And although they were very poor, they insisted on paying for all the supplies they used at that time.

R. L. S. did his best to persuade them not to make him such a generous gift. But they insisted, and after many days of hard work, the road was finished. The chiefs wanted to call it the Road of the Loving Heart. But Stevenson said it should be known as the Road of Gratitude. When it was declared open, all the chiefs wanted their names and titles painted on a board set up at the crossroads. With the names was this inscription:

> *"Considering the great love of Tusitala in his loving care of us in our distress in the prison, we have therefore prepared a splendid gift. It shall never be muddy. It shall endure forever, this road that we have dug."*

CHAPTER EIGHTEEN

Home Is the Sailor

LIFE was very happy at Vailima during the late autumn of 1894. On November 13th, the Samoan chiefs gave Louis a great feast.

Two years before that, Louis had given away his birthday to little Annie Ide, who lived on the island. Annie's real birthday was December 25th. But she had often complained that it was not fair to have one's birthday fall on Christmas Day. It robbed a person of a Special Occasion every year.

"You may have my birthday," Stevenson told her, and then he wrote her a letter as proof that he had given his birthday away.

Annie was very proud of having Louis' birthday as her own. She planned to keep it and celebrate it every year of her life. When

[*171*]

she had no further use for it, Louis said jokingly that she must pass it on to the President of the United States.

So November 13th was no longer properly Louis' birthday at all. But he was forty-four on that day in 1894, and the Samoan chiefs honored him with a very fine feast. Everyone at the feast was very gay. They ate a great deal, and then there were speeches in English and Samoan.

On December 3rd, Louis was still in wonderful spirits. But for some reason that she could not explain, Fanny felt nervous and unhappy.

Louis tried to cheer her by reading what he had written that day of his new story, *Weir of Hermiston*. He thought it was going to be his best book yet. Not long before, his friends in Scotland had written him that they were bringing out a handsome edition of all his works, to be called the Edinburgh Edition. Louis talked about that, trying to cheer his wife. He reminded her that next year perhaps his cousin Bob could come to Samoa to visit them.

At last, when Fanny still seemed melancholy, Louis went to the cellar and found a

[*172*]

special bottle of wine, which he carried to the veranda where his wife was sitting.

"We shall celebrate this evening with a little feast, Fanny," he said. "I will mix the salad myself. You know I have a gift for making salads . . ."

Fanny tried to smile.

Louis was still talking eagerly when suddenly he put his hands to his head. "What's that?" he asked sharply, and then he fell unconscious on the veranda. Fanny sprang to help him, calling out to one of the servants. Doctors were summoned at once. But two hours later Robert Louis Stevenson was dead.

The household who called themselves the Clan Tusitala knelt around the couch where he lay wrapped in the Union Jack that had flown all day over Vailima. Members of the Samoan tribes filed past, bringing their precious finely woven mats that had been in their families for generations. They laid the mats over the Union Jack.

"*Talofa,* Tusitala!" Each Samoan murmured his farewell.

One of Mataafa's old chiefs spoke for them all:

"Sleep, Tusitala! I am poor and can give

[*173*]

nothing this last day he receives his friends.
Yet I am not afraid to look for the last time
in my friend's face, never to see him more till
we meet with God . . . When Mataafa was
taken, who was our support but Tusitala? We
were in prison, and he cared for us. We were
sick, and he made us well. We were hungry,
and he fed us. The day was no longer than his
kindness."

Lloyd told the men that Tusitala had said he would like to be buried on the top of Mount Vaea. From there one could look out far over the sea. But there was no way up the mountain through the tangle of scrub and brush.

With the dawn's first light, the Samoans started out to hew a track up the steep slope. Pola started with them.

"You'd better stay here, Pola," Belle told him, her eyes red with weeping. "You are only a little boy."

The slim, brown body stood very straight. "I am a Vailima man. Tusitala was my Chief. I go." And Pola went to work with the others.

By noon, the path was finished. Then, wearing wreaths of red flowers and bearing his coffin shoulder high upon their spears, the chiefs carried Tusitala to his last resting place.

All the inhabitants of the island, brown and white, of nearly every nationality, trudged through blazing heat up the narrow path to the ledge on top of the mountain. After a brief service, the most ancient of the chieftains stepped forward. Henceforth, he said, no firearms would ever be used on the mountain. So the birds that Tusitala loved to hear might still, without fear, sing around his grave.

EPILOGUE

The life of Robert Louis Stevenson was a short one as people reckon lives, being only forty-four years. But it was long in adventure. It is even longer in the memories of those to whom he has brought great joy.

The Teller of Tales still lives to every small child who listens to *The Child's Garden of Verses* at bedtime. He still lives to every boy and girl reading *Treasure Island* and his other stories.

In Edinburgh, in the Spec's clubrooms, they proudly display the Union Jack that flew from his yacht. His portrait is there with that of Sir Walter Scott—the Spec's two most distinguished members. There is a monument to him in St. Giles Cathedral.

Stamps have been issued with his portrait and others with a picture of Vailima on them. Donkeys all over the world have been named Modestine for the ornery little beast he traveled with.

When Annie Ide died as an old lady not long ago, the President of the United States accepted with a formal speech the birthday that Louis had given her.

More than sixty years after his death, Robert Louis Stevenson is remembered and honored. More important, he is still loved by children. And children, all his life long, were his favorite people.

His tomb is high on the Samoan mountain. Engraved on it are the verses he wrote

EPILOGUE

for his epitaph when he declared his address
was Death's Door:

"Under the wide and starry sky,
Dig the grave and let me lie,
Glad did I live and gladly die,
And I laid me down with a will.

This be the verse you grave for me:
Here he lies where he longed to be;
Home is the sailor, home from the sea;
And the hunter home from the hill."

About the Author

JOAN HOWARD was born in British Columbia, and she was destined to travel even as did Robert Louis Stevenson. Her childhood was spent in places as far apart as England and Alaska and India. Wherever the family moved, she took her beloved bull terrier and many cats. Pets were outnumbered only by books, and she learned more from reading than from school, although she did go to college later. She began to write stories when she was very young and has written many notable books for boys and girls, among them THE STORY OF LOUISA MAY ALCOTT, THE STORY OF MARK TWAIN, and THE STORY OF JOHN J. AUDUBON for Signature Books. She and her husband and son now live on their very own island in the Atlantic, complete with lighthouse and frolicking whales.

About the Artist

JO POLSENO lives in Westport, Connecticut, with his wife and three children. He put in three years of combat in Europe, four years studying fine arts, and has held numerous jobs that have given him valuable experience in his career as an artist. He has done advertising art, designed book jackets, and illustrated books for several publishers. He is now an instructor at the Famous Artist Course in Westport.

Signature Books

"Names That Made History"

ENID LaMONTE MEADOWCROFT, *Supervising Editor*